MW00650600

www.EffortlessMath.com

... So Much More Online!

✓ FREE Math lessons

✓ More Math learning books!

✓ Mathematics Worksheets

✓ Online Math Tutors

Need a PDF version of this book?

Please visit www.EffortlessMath.com

Praxis Core Math Prep 2020-2021

The Most Comprehensive Review and Ultimate Guide to the Praxis Core Math (5733) Test

By

Reza Nazari & Ava Ross

Copyright © 2020

Reza Nazari & Ava Ross

All rights reserved. No part of this publication may be reproduced, stored in a retrieval system, or transmitted in any form or by any means, electronic, mechanical, photocopying, recording, scanning, or otherwise, except as permitted under Section 107 or 108 of the 1976 United States Copyright Ac, without permission of the author.

All inquiries should be addressed to:

info@effortlessMath.com

www.EffortlessMath.com

ISBN: 978-1-64612-436-7

Published by: Effortless Math Education

www.EffortlessMath.com

Visit www.EffortlessMath.com

for Online Math Practice

Description

Praxis Core Math Prep 2020 – 2021, which reflects the 2020 - 2021 test guidelines, is dedicated to preparing test takers to ace the Praxis Core Math Test. This comprehensive Praxis Core Math Prep book with hundreds of examples, abundant sample Praxis Core mathematics questions, and two full-length and realistic Praxis Core Math tests is all you will ever need to fully prepare for the Praxis Core Math. It will help you learn everything you need to ace the math section of the Praxis Core test.

Effortless Math unique study program provides you with an in-depth focus on the math portion of the exam, helping you master the math skills that students find the most troublesome. This Praxis Core Math preparation book contains most common sample questions that are most likely to appear in the mathematics section of the Praxis Core.

Inside the pages of this comprehensive Praxis Core Math book, students can learn basic math operations in a structured manner with a complete study program to help them understand essential math skills. It also has many exciting features, including:

- ✓ Content 100% aligned with the 2020 Praxis Core test
- ✓ Written by Praxis Core Math instructors and test experts
- ✓ Complete coverage of all Praxis Core Math concepts and topics which you will be tested
- ✓ Over 2,500 additional Praxis Core math practice questions in both multiple-choice and grid-in formats with answers grouped by topic, so you can focus on your weak areas
- ✓ Abundant Math skill building exercises to help test-takers approach different question types that might be unfamiliar to them
- ✓ Exercises on different Praxis Core Math topics such as integers, percent, equations, polynomials, exponents and radicals
- ✓ 2 full-length practice tests (featuring new question types) with detailed answers

Praxis Core Math Prep 2020 – 2021 is an incredibly useful resource for those who want to review all topics being covered on the Praxis Core test. It efficiently and effectively reinforces learning outcomes through engaging questions and repeated practice, helping you to quickly master Math skills.

About the Author

Reza Nazari is the author of more than 100 Math learning books including:
– **Math and Critical Thinking Challenges:** For the Middle and High School Student
– **ACT Math in 30 Days**
– **ASVAB Math Workbook 2018 - 2019**
– **Effortless Math Education Workbooks**
– **and many more Mathematics books …**

Reza is also an experienced Math instructor and a test–prep expert who has been tutoring students since 2008. Reza is the founder of Effortless Math Education, a tutoring company that has helped many students raise their standardized test scores—and attend the colleges of their dreams. Reza provides an individualized custom learning plan and the personalized attention that makes a difference in how students view math.

You can contact Reza via email at:
reza@EffortlessMath.com

Find Reza's professional profile at:
goo.gl/zoC9rJ

Chapter 1:

Fractions and Mixed Numbers

Math Topics that you'll learn in this Chapter:

- ✓ Simplifying Fractions

- ✓ Adding and Subtracting Fractions

- ✓ Multiplying and Dividing Fractions

- ✓ Adding Mixed Numbers

- ✓ Subtracting Mixed Numbers

- ✓ Multiplying Mixed Numbers

- ✓ Dividing Mixed Numbers

Simplifying Fractions

☑ A fraction contains two numbers separated by a bar in between them. The bottom number, called the denominator, is the total number of equally divided portions in one whole. The top number, called the numerator, is how many portions you have. And the bar represents the operation of division.

☑ Simplifying a fraction means reducing it to lowest terms. To simplify a fraction, evenly divide both the top and bottom of the fraction by $2, 3, 5, 7, \ldots$ etc.

☑ Continue until you can't go any further.

Examples:

1) Simplify $\frac{12}{30}$

Solution: To simplify $\frac{12}{30}$, find a number that both 12 and 30 are divisible by.

Both are divisible by 6. Then: $\frac{12}{30} = \frac{12 \div 6}{30 \div 6} = \frac{2}{5}$

2) Simplify $\frac{64}{80}$

Solution: To simplify $\frac{64}{80}$, find a number that both 64 and 80 are divisible by.

Both are divisible by 8 and 16. Then: $\frac{64}{80} = \frac{64 \div 8}{80 \div 8} = \frac{8}{10}$, 8 and 10 are divisible by 2,

then: $\frac{8}{10} = \frac{4}{5}$ or $\frac{64}{80} = \frac{64 \div 16}{80 \div 16} = \frac{4}{5}$

3) Simplify $\frac{20}{60}$

Solution: To simplify $\frac{20}{60}$, find a number that both 20 and 60 are divisible by. Both are divisible by 20.

Then: $\frac{20}{60} = \frac{20 \div 20}{60 \div 20} = \frac{1}{3}$

Adding and Subtracting Fractions

✓ For "like" fractions (fractions with the same denominator), add or subtract the numerators (top numbers) and write the answer over the common denominator (bottom numbers).

✓ Adding and Subtracting fractions with the same denominator:

$$\frac{a}{b} + \frac{c}{b} = \frac{a+c}{b} \qquad\qquad \frac{a}{b} - \frac{c}{b} = \frac{a-c}{b}$$

✓ Find equivalent fractions with the same denominator before you can add or subtract fractions with different denominators.

✓ Adding and Subtracting fractions with different denominators:

$$\frac{a}{b} + \frac{c}{d} = \frac{ad+bc}{bd} \qquad\qquad \frac{a}{b} - \frac{c}{d} = \frac{ad-bc}{bd}$$

Examples:

1) Find the sum. $\frac{3}{4} + \frac{1}{3} =$

   Solution: These two fractions are "unlike" fractions. (they have different denominators). Use this formula: $\frac{a}{b} + \frac{c}{d} = \frac{ad+cb}{bd}$

   Then: $\frac{3}{4} + \frac{1}{3} = \frac{(3)(3)+(4)(1)}{4 \times 3} = \frac{9+4}{12} = \frac{13}{12}$

2) Find the difference. $\frac{4}{5} - \frac{3}{7} =$

   Solution: For "unlike" fractions, find equivalent fractions with the same denominator before you can add or subtract fractions with different denominators. Use this formula:

   $\frac{a}{b} - \frac{c}{d} = \frac{ad-bc}{bd}$

   $\frac{4}{5} - \frac{3}{7} = \frac{(4)(7)-(3)(5)}{5 \times 7} = \frac{28-15}{35} = \frac{13}{35}$

Multiplying and Dividing Fractions

☑ Multiplying fractions: multiply the top numbers and multiply the bottom numbers.

Simplify if necessary. $\frac{a}{b} \times \frac{c}{d} = \frac{a \times c}{b \times d}$

☑ Dividing fractions: Keep, Change, Flip

Keep first fraction, change division sign to multiplication, and flip the numerator

and denominator of the second fraction. Then, solve! $\frac{a}{b} \div \frac{c}{d} = \frac{a}{b} \times \frac{d}{c} = \frac{a \times d}{b \times c}$

Examples:

1) Multiply. $\frac{5}{8} \times \frac{2}{3} =$

Solution: Multiply the top numbers and multiply the bottom numbers.

$\frac{5}{8} \times \frac{2}{3} = \frac{5 \times 2}{8 \times 3} = \frac{10}{24}$, simplify: $\frac{10}{24} = \frac{10 \div 2}{24 \div 2} = \frac{5}{12}$

2) Solve. $\frac{1}{3} \div \frac{4}{7} =$

Solution: Keep first fraction, change division sign to multiplication, and flip the numerator and denominator of the second fraction.

Then: $\frac{1}{3} \div \frac{4}{7} = \frac{1}{3} \times \frac{7}{4} = \frac{1 \times 7}{3 \times 4} = \frac{7}{12}$

3) Calculate. $\frac{3}{5} \times \frac{2}{3} =$

Solution: Multiply the top numbers and multiply the bottom numbers.

$\frac{3}{5} \times \frac{2}{3} = \frac{3 \times 2}{5 \times 3} = \frac{6}{15}$, simplify: $\frac{6}{15} = \frac{6 \div 3}{15 \div 3} = \frac{2}{5}$

4) Solve. $\frac{1}{4} \div \frac{5}{6} =$

Solution: Keep first fraction, change division sign to multiplication, and flip the numerator and denominator of the second fraction.

Then: $\frac{1}{4} \div \frac{5}{6} = \frac{1}{4} \times \frac{6}{5} = \frac{1 \times 6}{4 \times 5} = \frac{6}{20}$, simplify: $\frac{6}{20} = \frac{6 \div 2}{20 \div 2} = \frac{3}{10}$

Adding Mixed Numbers

Use following steps for adding mixed numbers:

☑ Add whole numbers of the mixed numbers.

☑ Add the fractions of the mixed numbers.

☑ Find the Least Common Denominator (LCD) if necessary.

☑ Add whole numbers and fractions.

☑ Write your answer in lowest terms.

Examples:

1) Add mixed numbers. $3\frac{1}{3} + 1\frac{4}{5} =$

   Solution: Let's rewriting our equation with parts separated, $3\frac{1}{3} + 1\frac{4}{5} = 3 + \frac{1}{3} + 1 + \frac{4}{5}$. Now, add whole number parts: $3 + 1 = 4$

   Add the fraction parts $\frac{1}{3} + \frac{4}{5}$. Rewrite to solve with the equivalent fractions. $\frac{1}{3} + \frac{4}{5} = \frac{5}{15} + \frac{12}{15} = \frac{17}{15}$. The answer is an improper fraction (numerator is bigger than denominator). Convert the improper fraction into a mixed number: $\frac{17}{15} = 1\frac{2}{15}$. Now, combine the whole and fraction parts: $4 + 1\frac{2}{15} = 5\frac{2}{15}$

2) Find the sum. $1\frac{2}{5} + 2\frac{1}{2} =$

   Solution: Rewriting our equation with parts separated, $1 + \frac{2}{5} + 2 + \frac{1}{2}$. Add the whole number parts:

   $1 + 2 = 3$. Add the fraction parts: $\frac{2}{5} + \frac{1}{2} = \frac{4}{10} + \frac{5}{10} = \frac{9}{10}$

   Now, combine the whole and fraction parts: $3 + \frac{9}{10} = 3\frac{9}{10}$

Subtract Mixed Numbers

Use the following steps for subtracting mixed numbers.

☑ Convert mixed numbers into improper fractions. $a\frac{c}{b} = \frac{ab+c}{b}$

☑ Find equivalent fractions with the same denominator for unlike fractions. (fractions with different denominators)

☑ Subtract the second fraction from the first one. $\frac{a}{b} - \frac{c}{d} = \frac{ad-bc}{bd}$

☑ Write your answer in lowest terms.

☑ If the answer is an improper fraction, convert it into a mixed number.

Examples:

1) Subtract. $3\frac{4}{5} - 1\frac{3}{4} =$

Solution: Convert mixed numbers into fractions: $3\frac{4}{5} = \frac{3\times5+4}{5} = \frac{19}{5}$ and $1\frac{3}{4} = \frac{1\times4+3}{4} = \frac{7}{4}$
These two fractions are "unlike" fractions. (they have different denominators). Find equivalent fractions with the same denominator. Use this formula: $\frac{a}{b} - \frac{c}{d} = \frac{ad-bc}{bd}$
$\frac{19}{5} - \frac{7}{4} = \frac{(19)(4)-(5)(7)}{5\times4} = \frac{76-35}{20} = \frac{41}{20}$, the answer is an improper fraction, convert it into a mixed number. $\frac{41}{20} = 2\frac{1}{20}$

2) Subtract. $4\frac{3}{8} - 1\frac{1}{2} =$

Solution: Convert mixed numbers into fractions: $4\frac{3}{8} = \frac{4\times8+3}{8} = \frac{35}{8}$ and $1\frac{1}{2} = \frac{1\times2+1}{4} = \frac{3}{2}$
Find equivalent fractions: $\frac{3}{2} = \frac{12}{8}$. Then: $4\frac{3}{8} - 1\frac{1}{2} = \frac{35}{8} - \frac{12}{8} = \frac{23}{8}$
The answer is an improper fraction, convert it into a mixed number.
$$\frac{23}{8} = 2\frac{7}{8}$$

Multiplying Mixed Numbers

Use following steps for multiplying mixed numbers:

☑ Convert the mixed numbers into fractions. $a\frac{c}{b} = a + \frac{c}{b} = \frac{ab+c}{b}$

☑ Multiply fractions. $\frac{a}{b} \times \frac{c}{d} = \frac{a \times c}{b \times d}$

☑ Write your answer in lowest terms.

☑ If the answer is an improper fraction (numerator is bigger than denominator), convert it into a mixed number.

Examples:

1) Multiply. $3\frac{1}{3} \times 4\frac{1}{6} =$

   Solution: Convert mixed numbers into fractions, $3\frac{1}{3} = \frac{3 \times 3 + 1}{3} = \frac{10}{3}$ and $4\frac{1}{6} = \frac{4 \times 6 + 1}{6} = \frac{25}{6}$

   Apply the fractions rule for multiplication, $\frac{10}{3} \times \frac{25}{6} = \frac{10 \times 25}{3 \times 6} = \frac{250}{18}$

   The answer is an improper fraction. Convert it into a mixed number. $\frac{250}{18} = 13\frac{8}{9}$

2) Multiply. $2\frac{1}{2} \times 3\frac{2}{3} =$

   Solution: Converting mixed numbers into fractions, $2\frac{1}{2} \times 3\frac{2}{3} = \frac{5}{2} \times \frac{11}{3}$

   Apply the fractions rule for multiplication, $\frac{5}{2} \times \frac{11}{3} = \frac{5 \times 11}{2 \times 3} = \frac{55}{6} = 9\frac{1}{6}$

3) Multiply mixed numbers. $2\frac{1}{3} \times 2\frac{1}{2} =$

   Solution: Converting mixed numbers to fractions, $2\frac{1}{3} = \frac{7}{3}$ and $2\frac{1}{2} = \frac{5}{2}$. Multiply two fractions:

   $$\frac{7}{3} \times \frac{5}{2} = \frac{7 \times 5}{3 \times 2} = \frac{35}{6} = 5\frac{5}{6}$$

Dividing Mixed Numbers

Use following steps for dividing mixed numbers:

☑ Convert the mixed numbers into fractions. $a\frac{c}{b} = a + \frac{c}{b} = \frac{ab+c}{b}$

☑ Divide fractions: Keep, Change, Flip: Keep first fraction, change division sign to multiplication, and flip the numerator and denominator of the second fraction. Then, solve! $\frac{a}{b} \div \frac{c}{d} = \frac{a}{b} \times \frac{d}{c} = \frac{a \times d}{b \times c}$

☑ Write your answer in lowest terms.

☑ If the answer is an improper fraction (numerator is bigger than denominator), convert it into a mixed number.

Examples:

1) Solve. $3\frac{2}{3} \div 2\frac{1}{2}$

Solution: Convert mixed numbers into fractions: $3\frac{2}{3} = \frac{3\times3+2}{3} = \frac{11}{3}$ and $2\frac{1}{2} = \frac{2\times2+1}{2} = \frac{5}{2}$

Keep, Change, Flip: $\frac{11}{3} \div \frac{5}{2} = \frac{11}{3} \times \frac{2}{5} = \frac{11\times2}{3\times5} = \frac{22}{15}$. The answer is an improper fraction. Convert it into a mixed number: $\frac{22}{15} = 1\frac{7}{15}$

2) Solve. $3\frac{4}{5} \div 1\frac{5}{6}$

Solution: Convert mixed numbers to fractions, then solve:

$3\frac{4}{5} \div 1\frac{5}{6} = \frac{19}{5} \div \frac{11}{6} = \frac{19}{5} \times \frac{6}{11} = \frac{114}{55} = 2\frac{4}{55}$

3) Solve. $2\frac{2}{7} \div 2\frac{3}{5}$

Solution: Converting mixed numbers to fractions: $3\frac{4}{5} \div 1\frac{5}{6} = \frac{16}{7} \div \frac{13}{5}$

Keep, Change, Flip: $\frac{16}{7} \div \frac{13}{5} = \frac{16}{7} \times \frac{5}{13} = \frac{16\times5}{7\times13} = \frac{80}{91}$

Chapter 1: Practices

✎ *Simplify each fraction.*

1) $\dfrac{18}{30} =$

2) $\dfrac{21}{42} =$

3) $\dfrac{35}{55} =$

4) $\dfrac{48}{72} =$

5) $\dfrac{54}{81} =$

6) $\dfrac{80}{200} =$

✎ *Find the sum or difference.*

7) $\dfrac{6}{15} + \dfrac{3}{15} =$

8) $\dfrac{2}{3} + \dfrac{1}{9} =$

9) $\dfrac{1}{4} + \dfrac{2}{5} =$

10) $\dfrac{7}{10} - \dfrac{3}{10} =$

11) $\dfrac{1}{2} - \dfrac{3}{8} =$

12) $\dfrac{5}{7} - \dfrac{3}{5} =$

✎ *Find the answers.*

13) $\dfrac{1}{7} \div \dfrac{3}{8} =$

14) $\dfrac{2}{3} \times \dfrac{4}{7} =$

15) $\dfrac{5}{7} \times \dfrac{3}{4} =$

16) $\dfrac{2}{5} \div \dfrac{3}{7} =$

17) $\dfrac{3}{7} \div \dfrac{5}{8} =$

18) $\dfrac{3}{8} \times \dfrac{4}{7} =$

✎ *Calculate.*

19) $3\dfrac{1}{5} + 2\dfrac{2}{9} =$

20) $1\dfrac{1}{7} + 5\dfrac{2}{5} =$

21) $4\dfrac{4}{5} + 1\dfrac{2}{7} =$

22) $2\dfrac{4}{7} + 2\dfrac{3}{5} =$

23) $1\dfrac{5}{6} + 1\dfrac{2}{5} =$

24) $3\dfrac{5}{7} + 1\dfrac{2}{9} =$

✎ *Calculate.*

25) $3\frac{2}{5} - 1\frac{2}{9} =$ 27) $4\frac{2}{5} - 2\frac{2}{7} =$ 29) $9\frac{5}{7} - 7\frac{4}{21} =$

26) $5\frac{3}{5} - 1\frac{1}{7} =$ 28) $8\frac{3}{4} - 2\frac{1}{8} =$ 30) $11\frac{7}{12} - 9\frac{5}{6} =$

✎ *Find the answers.*

31) $1\frac{1}{8} \times 1\frac{3}{4} =$ 33) $2\frac{1}{8} \times 1\frac{2}{9} =$ 35) $1\frac{1}{2} \times 5\frac{2}{3} =$

32) $3\frac{1}{5} \times 2\frac{2}{7} =$ 34) $2\frac{3}{8} \times 2\frac{2}{5} =$ 36) $3\frac{1}{2} \times 6\frac{2}{3} =$

✎ *Solve.*

37) $9\frac{1}{2} \div 2\frac{3}{5} =$ 39) $5\frac{3}{4} \div 2\frac{2}{7} =$ 41) $7\frac{2}{5} \div 3\frac{3}{4} =$

38) $2\frac{3}{8} \div 1\frac{2}{5} =$ 40) $8\frac{1}{3} \div 4\frac{1}{4} =$ 42) $2\frac{4}{5} \div 3\frac{2}{3} =$

Answers – Chapter 1

1) $\frac{3}{5}$

2) $\frac{1}{2}$

3) $\frac{7}{11}$

4) $\frac{2}{3}$

5) $\frac{2}{3}$

6) $\frac{2}{5}$

7) $\frac{3}{5}$

8) $\frac{7}{9}$

9) $\frac{13}{20}$

10) $\frac{2}{5}$

11) $\frac{1}{8}$

12) $\frac{4}{35}$

13) $\frac{8}{21}$

14) $\frac{8}{21}$

15) $\frac{15}{28}$

16) $\frac{14}{15}$

17) $\frac{24}{35}$

18) $\frac{3}{14}$

19) $5\frac{19}{45}$

20) $6\frac{19}{35}$

21) $6\frac{3}{35}$

22) $5\frac{6}{35}$

23) $3\frac{7}{30}$

24) $4\frac{59}{63}$

25) $2\frac{8}{45}$

26) $6\frac{16}{35}$

27) $2\frac{4}{35}$

28) $6\frac{5}{8}$

29) $2\frac{11}{21}$

30) $1\frac{3}{4}$

31) $1\frac{31}{32}$

32) $7\frac{11}{35}$

33) $2\frac{43}{72}$

34) $5\frac{7}{10}$

35) $8\frac{1}{2}$

36) $23\frac{1}{3}$

37) $3\frac{17}{26}$

38) $1\frac{39}{56}$

39) $2\frac{33}{64}$

40) $1\frac{49}{51}$

41) $1\frac{73}{75}$

42) $\frac{42}{55}$

Chapter 2:

Decimals

Math Topics that you'll learn in this Chapter:

- ✓ Comparing Decimals
- ✓ Rounding Decimals
- ✓ Adding and Subtracting Decimals
- ✓ Multiplying and Dividing Decimals

Comparing Decimals

- Decimal is a fraction written in a special form. For example, instead of writing $\frac{1}{2}$ you can write 0.5

- A Decimal Number contains a Decimal Point. It separates the whole number part from the fractional part of a decimal number.

- Let's review decimal place values: Example: 53.9861

  5: tens   3: ones   9: tenths

  8: hundredths   6: thousandths   1: tens thousandths

☑ To compare decimals, compare each digit of two decimals in the same place value. Start from left. Compare hundreds, tens, ones, tenth, hundredth, etc.

☑ To compare numbers, use these symbols:

Equal to $=$,   Less than $<$,   Greater than $>$
Greater than or equal $\geq$,   Less than or equal $\leq$

Examples:

1) Compare 0.60 and 0.06.

   Solution: 0.60 *is greater than* 0.06, because the tenth place of 0.60 is 6, but the tenth place of 0.06 is zero. Then: $0.60 > 0.06$

2) Compare 0.0815 and 0.815.

   Solution: 0.815 *is greater than* 0.0815, because the tenth place of 0.815 is 8, but the tenth place of 0.0815 is zero. Then: $0.0815 < 0.815$

Rounding Decimals

☑ We can round decimals to a certain accuracy or number of decimal places. This is used to make calculation easier to do and results easier to understand, when exact values are not too important.

☑ First, you'll need to remember your place values: For example:

$$12.4869$$

1: tens	2: ones	4: tenths
8: hundredths	6: thousandths	9: tens thousandths

☑ To round a decimal, first find the place value you'll round to.

☑ Find the digit to the right of the place value you're rounding to. If it is 5 or bigger, add 1 to the place value you're rounding to and remove all digits on its right side. If the digit to the right of the place value is less than 5, keep the place value and remove all digits on the right.

Examples:

1) Round **1.9278** to the thousandth place value.

   Solution: First look at the next place value to the right, (tens thousandths). It's 8 and it is greater than 5. Thus add 1 to the digit in the thousandth place. Thousandth place is 7. → $7 + 1 = 8$, then, the answer is 1.928

2) Round **9.4126** to the nearest hundredth.

   Solution: First look at the digit to the right of hundredth (thousandths place value). It's 2 and it is less than 5, thus remove all the digits to the right of hundredth place. Then, the answer is 9.41

Adding and Subtracting Decimals

☑ Line up the decimal numbers.

☑ Add zeros to have same number of digits for both numbers if necessary.

☑ Remember your place values: For example:

$$73.5196$$

7: tens	3: ones	5: tenths
1: hundredths	9: thousandths	6: tens thousandths

☑ Add or subtract using column addition or subtraction.

Examples:

1) Add. $1.8 + 3.12$

   Solution: First line up the numbers: $\begin{array}{r} 1.8 \\ +3.12 \\ \hline \end{array}$ → Add a zero to have same number of digits for both numbers. $\begin{array}{r} 1.80 \\ +3.12 \\ \hline \end{array}$ → Start with the hundredths place: $0 + 2 = 2$, $\begin{array}{r} 1.80 \\ +3.12 \\ \hline 2 \end{array}$ → Continue with tenths place: $8 + 1 = 9$, $\begin{array}{r} 1.80 \\ +3.12 \\ \hline .92 \end{array}$ → Add the ones place: $3 + 1 = 4$, $\begin{array}{r} 1.80 \\ +3.12 \\ \hline 4.92 \end{array}$

2) Find the difference. $3.67 - 2.23$

   Solution: First line up the numbers: $\begin{array}{r} 3.67 \\ -2.23 \\ \hline \end{array}$ → Start with the hundredths place: $7 - 3 = 4$, $\begin{array}{r} 3.67 \\ -2.23 \\ \hline 4 \end{array}$ → Continue with tenths place. $6 - 2 = 4$, $\begin{array}{r} 3.67 \\ -2.23 \\ \hline .44 \end{array}$ → Subtract the ones place. $3 - 2 = 1$, $\begin{array}{r} 3.67 \\ -2.23 \\ \hline 1.44 \end{array}$

Praxis Core Math Prep 2020-2021

Multiplying and Dividing Decimals

For multiplying decimals:

☑ Ignore the decimal point and set up and multiply the numbers as you do with whole numbers.

☑ Count the total number of decimal places in both of the factors.

☑ Place the decimal point in the product.

For dividing decimals:

☑ If the divisor is not a whole number, move decimal point to right to make it a whole number. Do the same for dividend.

☑ Divide similar to whole numbers.

Examples:

1) Find the product. $0.81 \times 0.32 =$

   Solution: Set up and multiply the numbers as you do with whole numbers. Line up the numbers: $\begin{array}{r} 81 \\ \times 32 \end{array}$ → Start with the ones place then continue with other digits → $\begin{array}{r} 81 \\ \times 32 \\ \hline 2,592 \end{array}$. Count the total number of decimal places in both of the factors. There are four decimals digits. (two for each factor 0.81 and 0.32) Then: $0.81 \times 0.32 = 0.2592$

2) Find the quotient. $1.60 \div 0.4 =$

   Solution: The divisor is not a whole number. Multiply it by 10 to get 4: $\rightarrow 0.4 \times 10 = 4$

   Do the same for the dividend to get 16. $\rightarrow 1.60 \times 10 = 1.6$

   Now, divide: $16 \div 4 = 4$. The answer is 4.

Chapter 2: Practices

✎ *Compare. Use* >, =, *and* <

1) 0.88 ☐ 0.088

2) 0.56 ☐ 0.57

3) 0.99 ☐ 0.89

4) 1.55 ☐ 1.65

5) 1.58 ☐ 1.75

6) 2.91 ☐ 2.85

✎ *Round each decimal to the nearest whole number.*

7) 5.94

8) 16.47

9) 9.7

10) 35.8

11) 24.46

12) 12.5

✎ *Find the sum or difference.*

13) $43.15 + 23.65 =$

14) $56.74 - 22.43 =$

15) $25.47 + 31.76 =$

16) $69.87 - 35.98 =$

17) $45.53 + 18.95 =$

18) $25.13 - 18.72 =$

✎ *Find the product and quotient.*

19) $0.5 \times 0.8 =$

20) $6.4 \div 0.4 =$

21) $3.25 \times 2.2 =$

22) $8.4 \div 2.5 =$

23) $5.4 \times 0.6 =$

24) $1.42 \div 0.5 =$

Answers – Chapter 2

1) $0.88 > 0.088$
2) $0.56 < 0.57$
3) $0.99 > 0.89$
4) $1.55 < 1.65$
5) $1.58 < 1.75$
6) $2.91 > 2.85$
7) 6
8) 16
9) 10
10) 36
11) 24
12) 13

13) 66.8
14) 34.31
15) 57.23
16) 33.89
17) 64.48
18) 6.41
19) 0.4
20) 16
21) 7.15
22) 3.36
23) 3.24
24) 2.84

Chapter 3:

Integers and Order of Operations

Math Topics that you'll learn in this Chapter:

- ✓ Adding and Subtracting Integers

- ✓ Multiplying and Dividing Integers

- ✓ Order of Operations

- ✓ Integers and Absolute Value

Adding and Subtracting Integers

☑ Integers include: zero, counting numbers, and the negative of the counting numbers. $\{... , -3, -2, -1, 0, 1, 2, 3, ...\}$

☑ Add a positive integer by moving to the right on the number line. (you will get a bigger number)

☑ Add a negative integer by moving to the left on the number line. (you will get a smaller number)

☑ Subtract an integer by adding its opposite.

Examples:

1) Solve. $(-4) - (-5) =$

   Solution: Keep the first number and convert the sign of the second number to its opposite. (change subtraction into addition. Then: $(-4) + 5 = 1$

2) Solve. $11 + (8 - 19) =$

   Solution: First subtract the numbers in brackets, $8 - 19 = -11$.

   Then: $11 + (-11) = \rightarrow$ change addition into subtraction: $11 - 11 = 0$

3) Solve. $5 - (-14 - 3) =$

   Solution: First subtract the numbers in brackets, $-14 - 3 = -17$

   Then: $5 - (-17) = \rightarrow$ change subtraction into addition: $5 + 17 = 22$

4) Solve. $10 + (-6 - 15) =$

   Solution: First subtract the numbers in brackets, $-6 - 15 = -21$

   Then: $10 + (-21) = \rightarrow$ change addition into subtraction: $10 - 21 = -11$

Multiplying and Dividing Integers

Use following rules for multiplying and dividing integers:

☑ (negative) × (negative) = positive

☑ (negative) ÷ (negative) = positive

☑ (negative) × (positive) = negative

☑ (negative) ÷ (positive) = negative

☑ (positive) × (positive) = positive

☑ (positive) ÷ (negative) = negative

Examples:

1) Solve. $2 \times (-3) =$

   Solution: Use this rule: (positive) × (negative) = negative.
   Then: $(2) \times (-3) = -6$

2) Solve. $(-5) + (-27 \div 9) =$

   Solution: First divided -27 by 9, the numbers in brackets, use this rule:
   (negative) ÷ (positive) = negative. Then: $-27 \div 9 = -3$
   $(-5) + (-27 \div 9) = (-5) + (-3) = -5 - 3 = -8$

3) Solve. $(15 - 17) \times (-8) =$

   Solution: First subtract the numbers in brackets, $15 - 17 = -2 \rightarrow (-2) \times (-8) =$

   Now use this rule: (negative) × (negative) = positive
   $(-2) \times (-8) = 16$

4) Solve. $(16 - 10) \div (-2) =$

   Solution: First subtract the numbers in brackets, $16 - 10 = 6 \rightarrow (6) \div (-2) =$

   Now use this rule: (positive) ÷ (negative) = negative
   $(6) \div (-2) = -3$

Order of Operations

☑ In Mathematics, "operations" are addition, subtraction, multiplication, division, exponentiation (written as b^n), and grouping;

☑ When there is more than one math operation in an expression, use PEMDAS: (to memorize this rule, remember the phrase "Please Excuse My Dear Aunt Sally".)

- ❖ Parentheses
- ❖ Exponents
- ❖ Multiplication and Division (from left to right)
- ❖ Addition and Subtraction (from left to right)

Examples:

1) Calculate. $(3 + 5) \div (3^2 \div 9) =$

   Solution: First simplify inside parentheses: $(8) \div (9 \div 9) = (8) \div (1)$, Then: $(8) \div (1) = 8$

2) Solve. $(7 \times 8) - (12 - 4) =$

   Solution: First calculate within parentheses: $(7 \times 8) - (12 - 4) = (56) - (8)$, Then: $(56) - (8) = 48$

3) Calculate. $-2[(8 \times 9) \div (2^2 \times 2)] =$

   Solution: First calculate within parentheses: $-2[(72) \div (4 \times 2)] = -2[(72) \div (8)] = -2[9]$ multiply -2 and 9. Then: $-2[9] = -18$

4) Solve. $(14 \div 7) + (-13 + 8) =$

   Solution: First calculate within parentheses: $(14 \div 7) + (-13 + 8) = (2) + (-5)$

   Then: $(2) - (5) = -3$

Integers and Absolute Value

☑ The absolute value of a number is its distance from zero, in either direction, on the number line. For example, the distance of 9 and -9 from zero on number line is 9.

☑ The absolute value of an integer is the numerical value without its sign. (negative or positive)

☑ The vertical bar is used for absolute value as in $|x|$.

☑ The absolute value of a number is never negative; because it only shows, "how far the number is from zero".

Examples:

1) Calculate. $|12 - 4| \times 4 =$

Solution: First solve $|12 - 4|$, $\rightarrow |12 - 4| = |8|$, the absolute value of 8 is 8, $|8| = 8$
Then: $8 \times 4 = 32$

2) Solve. $\frac{|-16|}{4} \times |3 - 8| =$

Solution: First find $|-16|$, $\rightarrow$ the absolute value of -16 is 16, then: $|-16| = 16$,
$\frac{16}{4} \times |3 - 8| =$
Now, calculate $|3 - 8|$, $\rightarrow |3 - 8| = |-5|$, the absolute value of -5 is 5. $|-5| = 5$
Then: $\frac{16}{4} \times 5 = 4 \times 5 = 20$

3) Solve. $|9 - 3| \times \frac{|-3 \times 8|}{6} =$

Solution: First calculate $|9 - 3|$, $\rightarrow |9 - 3| = |6|$, the absolute value of 6 is 6, $|6| = 6$. Then:
$6 \times \frac{|-3 \times 8|}{6}$
Now calculate $|-3 \times 8|$, $\rightarrow |-3 \times 8| = |-24|$, the absolute value of -24 is 24, $|-24| = 24$
Then: $6 \times \frac{24}{6} = 6 \times 4 = 24$

Chapter 3: Practices

✍ *Find each sum or difference.*

1) $18 + (-5) =$

2) $(-16) + 24 =$

3) $(-12) + (-9) =$

4) $14 + (-8) + 6 =$

5) $24 + (-10 - 7) =$

6) $(-15) + (-6 + 12) =$

✍ *Find each product or quotient.*

7) $8 \times (-6) =$

8) $(-12) \div (-3) =$

9) $(-4) \times (-7) \times 2 =$

10) $3 \times (-5) \times (-6) =$

11) $(-7 - 37) \div (-11) =$

12) $(8 - 6) \times (-24) =$

✍ *Evaluate each expression.*

13) $8 + (3 \times 7) =$

14) $(18 \times 2) - 14 =$

15) $(15 - 7) + (2 \times 6) =$

16) $(8 + 4) \div (2^3 \div 2) =$

17) $2[(6 \times 3) \div (3^2 \times 2)] =$

18) $-3[(8 \times 2^2) \div (8 \times 2)] =$

✍ *Find the answers.*

19) $|-6| + |9 - 12| =$

20) $|8| - |7 - 19| + 1 =$

21) $\frac{|-40|}{8} \times \frac{|-1\ |}{5} =$

22) $|7 \times -5| \times \frac{|-32|}{8} =$

23) $\frac{|-121|}{11} - |-8 \times 2| =$

24) $\frac{|-3 \times -6|}{9} \times \frac{|4 \times -6|}{8} =$

Answers – Chapter 3

1) 13
2) 8
3) −21
4) 12
5) 7
6) −9
7) −48
8) 4
9) 56
10) 90
11) 4
12) −48

13) 29
14) 22
15) 20
16) 3
17) 2
18) −6
19) 9
20) −3
21) 15
22) 140
23) −5
24) 6

Chapter 4:

Ratios and Proportions

Math Topics that you'll learn in this Chapter:

- ✓ Simplifying Ratios

- ✓ Proportional Ratios

- ✓ Similarity and Ratios

Simplifying Ratios

☑ Ratios are used to make comparisons between two numbers.

☑ Ratios can be written as a fraction, using the word "to", or with a colon. Example: $\frac{3}{4}$ or "3 to 4" or 3:4

☑ You can calculate equivalent ratios by multiplying or dividing both sides of the ratio by the same number.

Examples:

1) Simplify. $9:3 =$

   Solution: Both numbers 9 and 3 are divisible by 3 , $\Rightarrow 9 \div 3 = 3$, $3 \div 3 = 1$, Then: $9:3 = 3:1$

2) Simplify. $\frac{24}{44} =$

   Solution: Both numbers 24 and 44 are divisible by 4, $\Rightarrow 24 \div 4 = 6, 44 \div 4 = 11$, Then: $\frac{24}{44} = \frac{6}{11}$

3) There are 36 students in a class and 16 of them are girls. Write the ratio of girls to boys.

   Solution: Subtract 16 from 36 to find the number of boys in the class. $36 - 16 = 20$. There are 20 boys in the class. So, ratio of girls to boys is $16:20$. Now, simplify this ratio. Both 20 and 16 are divisible by 4. Then: $20 \div 4 = 5$, and $16 \div 4 = 4$. In simplest form, this ratio is $4:5$

4) A recipe calls for butter and sugar in the ratio $3:4$. If you're using 9 cups of butter, how many cups of sugar should you use?

   Solution: Since, you use 9 cups of butter, or 3 times as much, you need to multiply the amount of sugar by 3. Then: $4 \times 3 = 12$. So, you need to use 12 cups of sugar. You can solve this using equivalent fractions: $\frac{3}{4} = \frac{9}{12}$

Praxis Core Math Prep 2020-2021

Proportional Ratios

☑ Two ratios are proportional if they represent the same relationship.

☑ A proportion means that two ratios are equal. It can be written in two

ways: $\frac{a}{b} = \frac{c}{d}$ $a : b = c : d$

☑ The proportion $\frac{a}{b} = \frac{c}{d}$ can be written as: $a \times d = c \times b$

Examples:

1) Solve this proportion for x. $\frac{3}{7} = \frac{12}{x}$

   Solution: Use cross multiplication: $\frac{3}{7} = \frac{12}{x} \Rightarrow 3 \times x = 7 \times 12 \Rightarrow 3x = 84$

   Divide both sides by 3 to find x: $x = \frac{84}{3} \Rightarrow x = 28$

2) If a box contains red and blue balls in ratio of $3 : 7$ red to blue, how many red balls are there if 49 blue balls are in the box?

   Solution: Write a proportion and solve. $\frac{3}{7} = \frac{x}{49}$

   Use cross multiplication: $3 \times 49 = 7 \times x \Rightarrow 147 = 7x$

   Divide to find x: $x = \frac{147}{7} \Rightarrow x = 21$. There are 21 red balls in the box.

3) Solve this proportion for x. $\frac{2}{9} = \frac{12}{x}$

   Solution: Use cross multiplication: $\frac{2}{9} = \frac{12}{x} \Rightarrow 2 \times x = 9 \times 12 \Rightarrow 2x = 108$

   Divide to find x: $x = \frac{108}{2} \Rightarrow x = 54$

4) Solve this proportion for x. $\frac{6}{7} = \frac{18}{x}$

   Solution: Use cross multiplication: $\frac{6}{7} = \frac{18}{x} \Rightarrow 6 \times x = 7 \times 18 \Rightarrow 6x = 126$

   Divide to find x: $x = \frac{126}{6} \Rightarrow x = 21$

Similarity and Ratios

☑ Two figures are similar if they have the same shape.

☑ Two or more figures are similar if the corresponding angles are equal, and the corresponding sides are in proportion.

Examples:

1) Following triangles are similar. What is the value of unknown side?

Solution: Find the corresponding sides and write a proportion.

$\frac{5}{10} = \frac{4}{x}$. Now, use cross product to solve for x:

$\frac{5}{10} = \frac{4}{x} \rightarrow 5 \times x = 10 \times 4 \rightarrow 5x = 40$. Divide

both sides by 5. Then: $5x = 40 \rightarrow \frac{5x}{5} = \frac{40}{5} \rightarrow x =$

8

The missing side is 8.

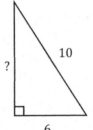

2) Two rectangles are similar. The first is 6 feet wide and 20 feet long. The second is 15 feet wide. What is the length of the second rectangle?

Solution: Let's put x for the length of the second rectangle. Since two rectangles are similar, their corresponding sides are in proportion. Write a proportion and solve for the missing

number. $\frac{6}{15} = \frac{20}{x} \rightarrow 6x = 15 \times 20 \rightarrow 6x = 300 \rightarrow x = \frac{300}{6} = 50$

The length of the second rectangle is 50 feet.

Chapter 4: Practices

✎ *Reduce each ratio.*

1) $9:18 = $ ___:___
2) $6:54 = $ ___:___
3) $28:49 = $ ___:___
4) Bob has 12 red cards and 20 green cards. What is the ratio of Bob's red cards to his green cards? _____

5) In a party, 10 soft drinks are required for every 12 guests. If there are 252 guests, how many soft drinks is required? _____

6) In Jack's class, 18 of the students are tall and 10 are short. In Michael's class 54 students are tall and 30 students are short. Which class has a higher ratio of tall to short students? _____

✎ *Solve each proportion.*

7) $\frac{3}{7} = \frac{18}{x}, x = $ ____

8) $\frac{5}{9} = \frac{x}{108}, x = $ ____

9) $\frac{2}{13} = \frac{8}{x}, x = $ ____

10) $\frac{4}{10} = \frac{6}{x}, x = $ ____

11) $\frac{8}{20} = \frac{x}{65}, x = $ ____

12) $\frac{6}{15} = \frac{14}{x}, x = $ ____

✎ *Solve each problem.*

13) Two rectangles are similar. The first is $8\,feet$ wide and $22\,feet$ long. The second is $12\,feet$ wide. What is the length of the second rectangle? _____

14) Two rectangles are similar. One is $3.2\,meters$ by $8\,meters$. The longer side of the second rectangle is $34.5\,meters$. What is the other side of the second rectangle? _____

Answers – Chapter 4

1) 1 : 2

2) 1 : 9

3) 4 : 7

4) 3 : 5

5) 210

6) The ratio for both classes is 9 to 5.

7) 42

8) 60

9) 52

10) 15

11) 26

12) 35

13) 33 feet

14) 13.8 meters

Chapter 5:

Percentage

Math Topics that you'll learn in this Chapter:

- ✓ Percentage Calculations

- ✓ Percent Problems

- ✓ Percent of Increase and Decrease

- ✓ Discount, Tax and Tip

- ✓ Simple Interest

Percent Problems

☑ Percent is a ratio of a number and 100. It always has the same denominator, 100. Percent symbol is "%".

☑ Percent means "per 100". So, 20% is 20/100.

☑ In each percent problem, we are looking for the base, or part or the percent.

☑ Use the following equations to find each missing section in a percent problem:

- Base = Part ÷ Percent
- Part = Percent × Base
- Percent = Part ÷ Base

Examples:

1) What is 25% of 60?

Solution: In this problem, we have percent (25%) and base (60) and we are looking for the "part".

Use this formula: $part = percent \times base$. Then: $part = 25\% \times 60 = \frac{25}{100} \times 60 = 0.25 \times 60 = 15$.

The answer:

25% of 60 is 15.

2) 20 is what percent of 400?

Solution: In this problem, we are looking for the percent. Use this equation:

$Percent = Part \div Base \rightarrow Percent = 20 \div 400 = 0.05 = 5\%$.

Then: 20 is 5 percent of 400.

Percent of Increase and Decrease

☑ Percent of change (increase or decrease) is a mathematical concept that represents the degree of change over time.

☑ To find the percentage of increase or decrease:

1. New Number – Original Number

2. The result ÷ Original Number × 100

☑ Or use this formula: Percent of change = $\frac{new\ number - original\ number}{original\ number} \times 100$

☑ Note: If your answer is a negative number, then this is a percentage decrease. If it is positive, then this is a percentage increase.

Examples:

1) The price of a shirt increases from \$20 to \$30. What is the percentage increase?
Solution: First find the difference: $30 - 20 = 10$
Then: $10 \div 20 \times 100 = \frac{10}{20} \times 100 = 50$. The percentage increase is 50. It means that the price of the shirt increased 50%.

2) The price of a table increased from \$25 to \$40. What is the percent of increase?
Solution: Use percentage formula: $Percent\ of\ change = \frac{new\ number - original\ number}{original\ number} \times$
$100 = \frac{40-25}{25} \times 100 = \frac{15}{25} \times 100 = 0.6 \times 100 = 60$. The percentage increase is 60. It means that the price of the table increased 60%.

3) The population of a town was 50,000 in the 2000 census and 40,000 in the 2010 census. By what percent did the population decrease?
Solution: Use percentage formula:
$Percent\ of\ change = \frac{new\ number - original\ number}{original\ number} \times 100 = \frac{40,000-50,000}{50,000} \times 100 = \frac{-10,000}{50,000} \times$
$100 = -0.2 \times 100 = -20$. The population of the town decreased by 20%.

Discount, Tax and Tip

☑ To find discount: Multiply the regular price by the rate of discount

☑ To find selling price: Original price – discount

☑ To find tax: Multiply the tax rate to the taxable amount (income, property value, etc.)

☑ To find tip, multiply the rate to the selling price.

Examples:

1) With an 10% discount, Ella was able to save $45 on a dress. What was the original price of the dress?

   Solution: let x be the original price of the dress. Then: $10 \% \ of \ x = 45$. Write an equation and solve for x: $0.10 \times x = 45 \rightarrow x = \frac{45}{0.10} = 450$. The original price of the dress was $450.

2) Sophia purchased a new computer for a price of $950 at the Apple Store. What is the total amount her credit card is charged if the sales tax is 7%?

   Solution: The taxable amount is $950, and the tax rate is 7%. Then: $Tax = 0.07 \times 950 = 66.50$

   $Final \ price = Selling \ price + Tax \rightarrow final \ price = \$950 + \$66.50 = \$1,016.50$

3) Nicole and her friends went out to eat at a restaurant. If their bill was $80.00 and they gave their server a 15% tip, how much did they pay altogether?

   Solution: First find the tip. To find tip, multiply the rate to the bill amount.

   $Tip = 80 \times 0.15 = 12$. The final price is: $\$80 + \$12 = \$92$

Simple Interest

☑ Simple Interest: The charge for borrowing money or the return for lending it.

☑ Simple interest is calculated on the initial amount (principal).

☑ To solve a simple interest problem, use this formula:

Interest = principal x rate x time $(I = p \times r \times t = prt)$

Examples:

1) Find simple interest for $300 investment at 6% for 5 years.

   Solution: Use Interest formula: $I = prt$ ($P = \$300$, r = 6% = $\frac{6}{100}$ = 0.06 and $t = 5$)
   Then: $I = 300 \times 0.06 \times 5 = \$90$

2) Find simple interest for $1,600 at 5% for 2 years.

   Solution: Use Interest formula: $I = prt$ ($P = \$1,600$, r = 5% = $\frac{5}{100}$ = 0.05 and $t = 2$)
   Then: $I = 1,600 \times 0.05 \times 2 = \$160$

3) Andy received a student loan to pay for his educational expenses this year. What is the interest on the loan if he borrowed $6,500 at 8% for 6 years?
   Solution: Use Interest formula: $I = prt$. $P = \$6,500$, r = 8% = 0.08 and $t = 6$

   Then: $I = 6,500 \times 0.08 \times 8 = \$3,120$

4) Bob is starting his own small business. He borrowed $10,000 from the bank at a 6% rate for 6 months. Find the interest Bob will pay on this loan.
   Solution: Use Interest formula: $I = prt$. $P = \$10,000$, r = 6% = 0.06 and $t = 0.5$ (6 months is half year). Then: $I = 10,000 \times 0.06 \times 0.5 = \$300$

Chapter 5: Practices

✍ *Solve each problem.*

1) 15 is what percent of 60? ___%

2) 18 is what percent of 24? ___%

3) 25 is what percent of 500? ___%

4) 14 is what percent of 280? ___%

5) 45 is what percent of 180? ___%

6) 70 is what percent of 350? ___%

✍ *Solve each percent of change word problem.*

7) Bob got a raise, and his hourly wage increased from $15 to $18. What is the percent increase? _____ %

8) The price of a pair of shoes increases from $40 to $66. What is the percent increase? ____ %

9) At a coffeeshop, the price of a cup of coffee increased from $1.20 to $1.44. What is the percent increase in the cost of the coffee? _____ %

✍ *Find the selling price of each item.*

10) Original price of a computer: $650

Tax: 8%, Selling price: $_____

11) Original price of a laptop: $480

Tax: 15%, Selling price: $_____

12) Nicolas hired a moving company. The company charged $400 for its services, and Nicolas gives the movers a 15% tip. How much does Nicolas tip the movers? $_____

13) Mason has lunch at a restaurant and the cost of his meal is $30. Mason wants to leave a 20% tip. What is Mason's total bill including tip? $_____

✎ *Determine the simple interest for these loans.*

14) $440 *at* 5% *for* 6 *years.* $___

15) $460 *at* 2.5% *for* 4 *years.* $__

16) $500 *at* 3% *for* 5 *years.* $___

17) $550 at 9% for 2 years. $___

18) A new car, valued at $28,000, depreciates at 9% per year. What is the value of the car one year after purchase? $_____

19) Sara puts $4,000 into an investment yielding 5% annual simple interest; she left the money in for five years. How much interest does Sara get at the end of those five years? $_____

Answers – Chapter 5

1) 25%
2) 75%
3) 5%
4) 5%
5) 25%
6) 20%
7) 20%
8) 65%
9) 20%
10) $702.00

11) $552.00
12) $60.00
13) $36.00
14) $132
15) $46
16) $75
17) $99
18) $25,480.00
19) $1,000.00

Chapter 6:

Expressions and Variables

Math Topics that you'll learn in this Chapter:

- ✓ Simplifying Variable Expressions
- ✓ Simplifying Polynomial Expressions
- ✓ The Distributive Property
- ✓ Evaluating One Variable
- ✓ Evaluating Two Variables

Simplifying Variable Expressions

☑ In algebra, a variable is a letter used to stand for a number. The most common letters are: $x, y, z, a, b, c, m, and\ n$.

☑ Algebraic expression is an expression contains integers, variables, and the math operations such as addition, subtraction, multiplication, division, etc.

☑ In an expression, we can combine "like" terms. (values with same variable and same power)

Examples:

1) Simplify. $(2x + 3x + 4) =$

   Solution: In this expression, there are three terms: $2x, 3x$, and 4. Two terms are "like terms": $2x$ and $3x$. Combine like terms. $2x + 3x = 5x$. Then: $(2x + 3x + 4) = 5x + 4$ (remember you cannot combine variables and numbers.)

2) Simplify. $12 - 3x^2 + 5x + 4x^2 =$

   Solution: Combine "like" terms: $-3x^2 + 4x^2 = x^2$. Then:
   $12 - 3x^2 + 5x + 4x^2 = 12 + x^2 + 5x$. Write in standard form (biggest powers first):
   $12 + x^2 + 5x = x^2 + 5x + 12$

3) Simplify. $(10x^2 + 2x^2 + 3x) =$

   Solution: Combine like terms. Then: $(10x^2 + 2x^2 + 3x) = 12x^2 + 3x$

4) Simplify. $15x - 3x^2 + 9x + 5x^2 =$

   Solution: Combine "like" terms: $15x + 9x = 24x$, and $-3x^2 + 5x^2 = 2x^2$

   Then: $15x - 3x^2 + 9x + 5x^2 = 24x + 2x^2$. Write in standard form (biggest powers first): $24x + 2x^2 = 2x^2 + 24x$

Praxis Core Math Prep 2020-2021

Simplifying Polynomial Expressions

☑ In mathematics, a polynomial is an expression consisting of variables and coefficients that involves only the operations of addition, subtraction, multiplication, and non-negative integer exponents of variables. $P(x) = a_n x^n + a_{n-1} x^{n-1} + \dots + a_2 x^2 + a_1 x + a_0$

☑ Polynomials must always be simplified as much as possible. It means you must add together any like terms. (values with same variable and same power)

Examples:

1) Simplify this Polynomial Expressions. $x^2 - 5x^3 + 2x^4 - 4x^3$

   Solution: Combine "like" terms: $-5x^3 - 4x^3 = -9x^3$

   Then: $x^2 - 5x^3 + 2x^4 - 4x^3 = x^2 - 9x^3 + 2x^4$

   Now, write the expression in standard form: $2x^4 - 9x^3 + x^2$

2) Simplify this expression. $(2x^2 - x^3) - (x^3 - 4x^2) =$

   Solution: First use distributive property: → multiply $(-)$ into $(x^3 - 4x^2)$

   $(2x^2 - x^3) - (x^3 - 4x^2) = 2x^2 - x^3 - x^3 + 4x^2$

   Then combine "like" terms: $2x^2 - x^3 - x^3 + 4x^2 = 6x^2 - 2x^3$

   And write in standard form: $6x^2 - 2x^3 = -2x^3 + 6x^2$

3) Simplify. $4x^4 - 5x^3 + 15x^4 - 12x^3 =$

   Solution: Combine "like" terms: $-5x^3 - 12x^3 = -17x^3$ and $4x^4 + 15x^4 = 19x^4$

   Then: $4x^4 - 5x^3 + 15x^4 - 12x^3 = 19x^4 - 17x^3$

The Distributive Property

☑ The distributive property (or the distributive property of multiplication over addition and subtraction) simplifies and solves expressions in the form of: $a(b + c)$ or $a(b - c)$

☑ The distributive property is multiplying a term outside the parentheses by the terms inside.

☑ Distributive Property rule: $a(b + c) = ab + ac$

Examples:

1) *Simply using distributive property.* $(-4)(x - 5)$

   Solution: Use Distributive Property rule: $a(b + c) = ab + ac$
   $(-4)(x - 5) = (-4 \times x) + (-4) \times (-5) = -4x + 20$

2) *Simply.* $(3)(2x - 4)$

   Solution: Use Distributive Property rule: $a(b + c) = ab + ac$
   $(3)(2x - 4) = (3 \times 2x) + (3) \times (-4) = 6x - 12$

3) *Simply.* $(-3)(3x - 5) + 4x$

   Solution: First, simplify $(-3)(3x - 5)$ using distributive property.
   Then: $(-3)(3x - 5) = -9x + 15$
   Now combine like terms: $(-3)(3x - 5) + 4x = -9x + 15 + 4x$
   In this expression, $-9x$ and $4x$ are "like terms" and we can combine them.
   $-9x + 4x = -5x$. Then: $-9x + 15 + 4x = -5x + 15$

Evaluating One Variable

✓ To evaluate one variable expressions, find the variable and substitute a number for that variable.

✓ Perform the arithmetic operations.

Examples:

1) *Calculate this expression for* $x = 3$. $15 - 3x$

   Solution: First substitute 3 for x

   Then: $15 - 3x = 15 - 3(3)$

   Now, use order of operation to find the answer: $15 - 3(3) = 15 - 9 = 6$

2) *Evaluate this expression for* $x = 1$. $5x - 12$

   Solution: First substitute 1 for x, then:

   $5x - 12 = 5(1) - 12$

   Now, use order of operation to find the answer: $5(1) - 12 = 5 - 12 = -7$

3) *Find the value of this expression when* $x = 5$. $25 - 4x$

   Solution: First substitute 5 for x, then:

   $25 - 4x = 25 - 4(5) = 25 - 20 = 5$

4) *Solve this expression for* $x = -2$. $12 + 3x$

   Solution: Substitute -2 for x, then: $12 + 3x = 12 + 3(-2) = 12 - 6 = 6$

Evaluating Two Variables

☑ To evaluate an algebraic expression, substitute a number for each variable.

☑ Perform the arithmetic operations to find the value of the expression.

Examples:

1) *Calculate this expression for* $a = 3$ *and* $b = -2$. $3a - 6b$

   Solution: First substitute 3 for a, and -2 for b , then:

   $$3a - 6b = 3(3) - 6(-2)$$

   Now, use order of operation to find the answer: $3(3) - 6(-2) = 9 + 12 = 21$

2) *Evaluate this expression for* $x = 3$ *and* $y = 1$. $3x + 5y$

   Solution: Substitute 3 for x, and 1 for y , then:

   $$3x + 5y = 3(3) + 5(1) = 9 + 5 = 14$$

3) *Find the value of this expression when* $a = 1$ *and* $b = 2$. $5(3a - 2b)$

   Solution: Substitute 1 for a, and 2 for b , then:

   $$5(3a - 2b) = 15a - 10b = 15(1) - 10(2) = 15 - 20 = -5$$

4) *Solve this expression.* $4x - 3y$, $x = 3$, $y = 5$

   Solution: Substitute 3 for x, and 5 for y and simplify. Then: $4x - 3y = 4(3) - 3(5) = 12 - 15 = -3$

Chapter 6: Practices

✍ **Simplify each expression.**

1) $(6x - 4x + 8 + 6) =$

2) $(-14x + 26x - 12) =$

3) $(24x - 6 - 18x + 3) =$

4) $5 + 8x^2 - 9 =$

5) $7x - 4x^2 + 6x =$

6) $15x^2 - 3x - 6x^2 + 4 =$

✍ **Simplify each polynomial.**

7) $2x^2 + 5x^3 - 7x^2 + 12x =$ _____

8) $2x^4 - 5x^5 + 8x^4 - 8x^2 =$ _____

9) $5x^3 + 15x - x^2 - 2x^3 =$ _____

10) $(8x^3 - 6x^2) + (9x^2 - 10x) =$ _____

11) $(12x^4 + 4x^3) - (8x^3 - 2x^4) =$ _____

12) $(9x^5 - 7x^3) - (5x^3 + x^2) =$ _____

✍ **Use the distributive property to simply each expression.**

13) $4(5 + 6x) =$

14) $5(8 - 4x) =$

15) $(-6)(2 - 9x) =$

16) $(-7)(6x - 4) =$

17) $(3x + 12)4 =$

18) $(8x - 5)(-3) =$

✍ **Evaluate each expression using the value given.**

19) $8 - x, x = -3$

20) $x + 12, x = -6$

21) $5x - 3, x = 2$

22) $4 - 6x, x = 1$

23) $3x + 1, x = -2$

24) $15 - 2x, x = 5$

✎ Evaluate each expression using the values given.

25) $4x - 2y, \ x = 4, y = -2$

26) $6a + 3b, \ a = 2, b = 4$

27) $12x - 5y - 8, \ x = 2, y = 3$

28) $-7a + 3b + 9, \ a = 4, b = 6$

29) $2x + 14 + 4y, \ x = 6, y = 8$

30) $4a - (5a - b) + 5, a = 4, b = 6$

Answers – Chapter 6

1) $2x + 14$
2) $12x - 12$
3) $6x - 3$
4) $8x^2 - 4$
5) $-4x^2 + 13x$
6) $9x^2 - 3x + 4$

7) $5x^3 - 5x^2 + 12x$
8) $-5x^5 + 10x^4 - 8x^2$
9) $3x^3 - x^2 + 15x$
10) $8x^3 + 3x^2 - 10x$
11) $14x^4 - 4x^3$
12) $9x^5 - 12x^3 - x^2$

13) $24x + 20$
14) $-20x + 40$
15) $54x - 12$
16) $-42x + 28$
17) $12x + 48$
18) $-24x + 15$

19) 11
20) 6
21) 7
22) -2
23) -5
24) 5

25) 20
26) 24
27) 1
28) -1
29) 58
30) 7

Chapter 7:

Equations and Inequalities

Math Topics that you'll learn in this Chapter:

- ✓ One–Step Equations

- ✓ Multi–Step Equations

- ✓ System of Equations

- ✓ Graphing Single–Variable Inequalities

- ✓ One–Step Inequalities

- ✓ Multi–Step Inequalities

One–Step Equations

☑ The values of two expressions on both sides of an equation are equal. Example: $ax = b$. In this equation, ax is equal to b.

☑ Solving an equation means finding the value of the variable.

☑ You only need to perform one Math operation in order to solve the one-step equations.

☑ To solve one-step equation, find the inverse (opposite) operation is being performed.

☑ The inverse operations are:

- Addition and subtraction
- Multiplication and division

Examples:

1) *Solve this equation for x.* $3x = 18, x = ?$

   Solution: Here, the operation is multiplication (variable x is multiplied by 3) and its inverse operation is division. To solve this equation, divide both sides of equation by 3:

   $$3x = 18 \rightarrow \frac{3x}{3} = \frac{18}{3} \rightarrow x = 6$$

2) *Solve this equation.* $x + 15 = 0, x = ?$

   Solution: In this equation 15 is added to the variable x. The inverse operation of addition is subtraction. To solve this equation, subtract 15 from both sides of the equation: $x + 15 - 15 = 0 - 15$. Then simplify: $x + 15 - 15 = 0 - 15 \rightarrow x = -15$

3) *Solve this equation for x.* $x - 23 = 0$

   Solution: Here, the operation is subtraction and its inverse operation is addition. To solve this equation, add 23 to both sides of the equation: $x + 23 - 23 = 0 - 23 \rightarrow x = -23$

Multi–Step Equations

☑ To solve a multi-step equation, combine "like" terms on one side.

☑ Bring variables to one side by adding or subtracting.

☑ Simplify using the inverse of addition or subtraction.

☑ Simplify further by using the inverse of multiplication or division.

☑ Check your solution by plugging the value of the variable into the original equation.

Examples:

1) *Solve this equation for* x. $3x + 6 = 16 - 2x$

   Solution: First bring variables to one side by adding $2x$ to both sides. Then:

   $3x + 6 = 16 - 2x \rightarrow 3x + 6 + 2x = 16 - 2x + 2x$. Simplify: $5x + 6 = 16$

   Now, subtract 6 from both sides of the equation: $5x + 6 - 6 = 16 - 6 \rightarrow 5x = 10 \rightarrow$

   Divide both sides by 5: $5x = 10 \rightarrow \frac{5x}{5} = \frac{10}{5} \rightarrow x = 2$

   Let's check this solution by substituting the value of 2 for x in the original equation:

   $\quad x = 2 \rightarrow 3x + 6 = 16 - 2x \rightarrow 3(2) + 6 = 16 - 2(2) \rightarrow 6 + 6 = 16 - 4 \rightarrow 12 = 12$

   The answer $x = 2$ is correct.

2) *Solve this equation for* x. $-4x + 4 = 16$

   Solution: Subtract 4 from both sides of the equation. $-4x + 4 - 4 = 16 - 4 \rightarrow -4x = 12$

   Divide both sides by -4, then: $-4x = 12 \rightarrow \frac{-4x}{-4} = \frac{12}{-4} \rightarrow x = -3$

   Now, check the solution: $x = -3 \rightarrow -4x + 4 = 16 \rightarrow -4(-3) + 4 = 16 \rightarrow 16 = 16$

   The answer $x = -2$ is correct.

System of Equations

✓ A system of equations contains two equations and two variables. For example, consider the system of equations: $x - y = 1, x + y = 5$

✓ The easiest way to solve a system of equations is using the elimination method. The elimination method uses the addition property of equality. You can add the same value to each side of an equation.

✓ For the first equation above, you can add $x + y$ to the left side and 5 to the right side of the first equation: $x - y + (x + y) = 1 + 5$. Now, if you simplify, you get: $x - y + (x + y) = 1 + 5 \rightarrow 2x = 6 \rightarrow x = 3$. Now, substitute 3 for the x in the first equation: $3 - y = 1$. By solving this equation, $y = 2$

Example:

What is the value of x + y in this system of equations? $\begin{cases} x + 2y = 6 \\ 2x - y = -8 \end{cases}$

Solution: Solving a System of Equations by Elimination:

Multiply the first equation by (-2), then add it to the second equation.

$$\begin{array}{l} -2(x + 2y = 6) \\ 2x - y = -8 \end{array} \Rightarrow \begin{array}{l} -2x - 4y = -12 \\ 2x - y = -8 \end{array} \Rightarrow -5y = -20 \Rightarrow y = 4$$

Plug in the value of y into one of the equations and solve for x.

$$x + 2(4) = 6 \Rightarrow x + 8 = 6 \Rightarrow x = 6 - 8 \Rightarrow x = -2$$

Thus, $x + y = -2 + 4 = 2$

Graphing Single–Variable Inequalities

☑ An inequality compares two expressions using an inequality sign.

☑ Inequality signs are: "less than" <, "greater than" >, "less than or equal to" ≤, and "greater than or equal to" ≥.

☑ To graph a single-variable inequality, find the value of the inequality on the number line.

☑ For less than (<) or greater than (>) draw open circle on the value of the variable. If there is an equal sign too, then use filled circle.

☑ Draw an arrow to the right for greater or to the left for less than.

Examples:

1) Draw a graph for this inequality. $x > 3$

Solution: Since, the variable is greater than 3, then we need to find 3 in the number line and draw an open circle on it.

Then, draw an arrow to the right.

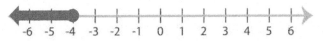

2) Graph this inequality. $x \leq -4$.

Solution: Since, the variable is less than or equal to −4, then we need to find −4 in the number line and draw a filled circle on it. Then, draw an arrow to the left.

Praxis Core Math Prep 2020-2021

One–Step Inequalities

☑ An inequality compares two expressions using an inequality sign.

☑ Inequality signs are: "less than" $<$, "greater than" $>$, "less than or equal to" $\leq$, and "greater than or equal to" $\geq$.

☑ You only need to perform one Math operation in order to solve the one-step inequalities.

☑ To solve one-step inequalities, find the inverse (opposite) operation is being performed.

☑ For dividing or multiplying both sides by negative numbers, flip the direction of the inequality sign.

Examples:

1) *Solve this inequality for* x. $x + 3 \geq 4$

   Solution: The inverse (opposite) operation of addition is subtraction. In this inequality, 3 is added to x. *To isolate x we need to* subtract 3 from both sides of the inequality. Then:

   $x + 3 \geq 4 \rightarrow x + 3 - 3 \geq 4 - 3 \rightarrow x \geq 1$. The solution is: $x \geq 1$

2) *Solve the inequality.* $x - 5 > -4$.

   Solution: 5 is subtracted from x. Add 5 to both sides. $x - 5 > -4 \rightarrow x - 5 + 5 > -4 + 5 \rightarrow x > 1$

3) *Solve.* $2x \leq -4$.

   Solution: 2 is multiplied to x. Divide both sides by 2. Then: $2x \leq -4 \rightarrow \frac{2x}{2} \leq \frac{-4}{2} \rightarrow x \leq -2$

4) *Solve.* $-6x \leq 12$.

   Solution: -6 is multiplied to x. Divide both sides by -6. Remember when dividing or multiplying both sides of an inequality by negative numbers, flip the direction of the inequality sign. Then:

   $$-6x \leq 12 \rightarrow \frac{-6x}{-6} \geq \frac{12}{-6} \rightarrow x \geq -2$$

Multi–Step Inequalities

☑ To solve a multi-step inequality, combine "like" terms on one side.

☑ Bring variables to one side by adding or subtracting.

☑ Isolate the variable.

☑ Simplify using the inverse of addition or subtraction.

☑ Simplify further by using the inverse of multiplication or division.

☑ For dividing or multiplying both sides by negative numbers, flip the direction of the inequality sign.

Examples:

1) *Solve this inequality.* $2x - 3 \leq 5$

   Solution: In this inequality, 3 is subtracted from $2x$. The inverse of subtraction is addition. Add 3 to both sides of the inequality: $2x - 3 + 3 \leq 5 + 3 \rightarrow 2x \leq 8$

   Now, divide both sides by 2. Then: $2x \leq 8 \rightarrow \frac{2x}{2} \leq \frac{8}{2} \rightarrow x \leq 4$

   The solution of this inequality is $x \leq 4$.

2) *Solve this inequality.* $3x + 9 < 12$

   Solution: First subtract 9 from both sides: $3x + 9 - 9 < 12 - 9$

   Then simplify: $3x + 9 - 9 < 12 - 9 \rightarrow 3x < 3$

   Now divide both sides by 3: $\frac{3x}{3} < \frac{3}{3} \rightarrow x < 1$

3) *Solve this inequality.* $-2x + 4 \geq 6$

   First subtract 4 from both sides: $-2x + 4 - 4 \geq 6 - 4 \rightarrow -2x \geq 2$

   Divide both sides by -2. Remember that you need to flip the direction of inequality sign.

   $$-2x \geq 2 \rightarrow \frac{-2x}{-2} \leq \frac{2}{-2} \rightarrow x \leq -1$$

Chapter 7: Practices

✎ **Solve each equation. (One–Step Equations)**

1) $x + 7 = 6, x =$ ____

2) $8 = 2 - x, x =$ ____

3) $-10 = 8 + x, x =$ ____

4) $x - 5 = -1, x =$ ____

5) $16 = x + 9, x =$ ____

6) $12 - x = -5, x =$ ____

✎ **Solve each equation. (Multi–Step Equations)**

7) $5(x + 3) = 20$

8) $-4(7 - x) = 16$

9) $8 = -2(x + 5)$

10) $14 = 3(4 - 2x)$

11) $5(x + 7) = -10$

12) $-2(6 + 3x) = 12$

✎ **Solve each system of equations.**

13) $-5x + y = -3$ $x =$

   $3x - 8y = 24$ $y =$

14) $3x - 2y = 2$ $x =$

   $x - y = 2$ $y =$

15) $4x + 7y = 2$ $x =$

   $6x + 7y = 10$ $y =$

16) $5x + 7y = 18$ $x =$

   $-3x + 7y = -22$ $y =$

✎ **Draw a graph for each inequality.**

17) $x \leq -2$

18) $x > -6$

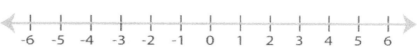

✎ *Solve each inequality and graph it.*

19) $x - 3 \geq -1$

20) $3x - 2 < 16$

✎ *Solve each inequality.*

21) $3x + 15 > -6$

22) $-18 + 4x \leq 10$

23) $4(x + 5) \geq 8$

24) $7x - 16 < 12$

25) $3(9 + x) \geq 15$

26) $-8 + 6x > 22$

Answers – Chapter 7

1) -1

2) -6

3) -18

7) 1

8) 11

9) -9

4) 4

5) 7

6) 17

10) $-\frac{1}{3}$

11) -9

12) -4

13) $x = 0$, $y = -3$

14) $x = -2$, $y = -4$

15) $x = 4$, $y = -2$

16) $x = 5$, $y = -1$

17)

18)

19)

20)

21) $x > -7$

22) $x \le 7$

23) $x \ge -3$

24) $x < 4$

25) $x \ge -4$

26) $x > 5$

Chapter 8:

Lines and Slope

Math Topics that you'll learn in this Chapter:

- ✓ Finding Slope

- ✓ Graphing Lines Using Slope–Intercept Form

- ✓ Writing Linear Equations

- ✓ Graphing Linear Inequalities

- ✓ Finding Midpoint

- ✓ Finding Distance of Two Points

Finding Slope

- ☑ The slope of a line represents the direction of a line on the coordinate plane.
- ☑ A coordinate plane contains two perpendicular number lines. The horizontal line is x and the vertical line is y. The point at which the two axes intersect is called the origin. An ordered pair (x, y) shows the location of a point.
- ☑ A line on coordinate plane can be drawn by connecting two points.
- ☑ To find the slope of a line, we need the equation of the line or two points on the line.
- ☑ The slope of a line with two points A (x_1, y_1) and B (x_2, y_2) can be found by using this formula: $\frac{y_2 - y_1}{x_2 - x_1} = \frac{rise}{run}$
- ☑ The equation of a line is typically written as $y = mx + b$ where m is the slope and b is the y-intercept.

Examples:

1) *Find the slope of the line through these two points*: $A(2, -7)$ and $B(4, 3)$.

   Solution: Slope $= \frac{y_2 - y_1}{x_2 - x_1}$. Let (x_1, y_1) be $A(2, -7)$ and (x_2, y_2) be $B(4, 3)$. (Remember, you can choose any point for (x_1, y_1) and (x_2, y_2)). *Then:* slope $= \frac{y_2 - y_1}{x_2 - x_1} = \frac{3 - (-7)}{4 - 2} = \frac{10}{2} = 5$

   The slope of the line through these two points is 5.

2) *Find the slope of the line with equation* $y = 3x + 6$

   Solution: when the equation of a line is written in the form of $y = mx + b$, the slope is m. In this line: $y = 3x + 6$, the slope is 3.

Graphing Lines Using Slope–Intercept Form

- ☑ Slope-intercept form of a line: given the slope m and the y-intercept (the intersection of the line and y-axis) b, then the equation of the line is: $y = mx + b$

- ☑ To draw the graph of a linear equation in slope-intercept form on the xy coordinate plane, find two points on the line by plugging two values for x and calculating the values of y.

- ☑ You can also use the slope (m) and one point to graph the line.

Example:

1) *Sketch the graph of* y = 2x − 4.

Solution: To graph this line, we need to find two points. When x is zero the value of y is -4. And when x is 2 the value of y is 0.

$$x = 0 \rightarrow y = 2(0) - 4 = -4,$$
$$y = 0 \rightarrow 0 = 2x - 4 \rightarrow x = 2$$

Now, we have two points: $(0, -4)$ and $(2, 0)$.

Find the points on the coordinate plane and graph the line. Remember that the slope of the line is 2.

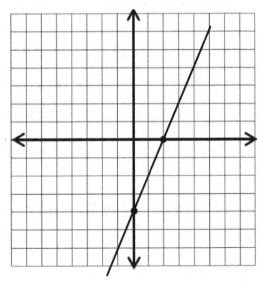

Writing Linear Equations

☑ The equation of a line in slope-intercept form: $y = mx + b$

☑ To write the equation of a line, first identify the slope.

☑ Find the y-intercept. This can be done by substituting the slope and the coordinates of a point (x, y) on the line.

Examples:

1) What is the equation of the line that passes through $(2, -4)$ and has a slope of 8?

Solution: The general slope-intercept form of the equation of a line is $y = mx + b$, where m is the slope and b is the y-intercept.

By substitution of the given point and given slope: $y = mx + b \rightarrow -4 = (2)(8) + b$

So, $b = -4 - 16 = -20$, and the required equation is $y = 8x - 20$

2) Write the equation of the line through two points $A(2, 1)$ and $B(-2, 5)$.

Solution: Fist find the slope: $Slop = \frac{y_2 - y_1}{x_2 - x_1} = \frac{5 - 1}{-2 - 2} = \frac{4}{-4} = -1 \rightarrow m = -1$

To find the value of b, use either points and plug in the values of x and y in the equation. The answer will be the same: $y = -x + b$. Let's check both points. Then:

$(2, 1) \rightarrow y = mx + b \rightarrow 1 = -1(2) + b \rightarrow b = 3$

$(-2, 5) \rightarrow y = mx + b \rightarrow 5 = -1(-2) + b \rightarrow b = 3$. The y-intercept of the line is 3.

The equation of the line is: $y = -x + 3$

3) What is the equation of the line that passes through $(2, -1)$ and has a slope of 5?

Solution: The general slope-intercept form of the equation of a line is $y = mx + b$, where m is the slope and b is the y-intercept.

By substitution of the given point and given slope: $y = mx + b \rightarrow -1 = (5)(2) + b$

So, $b = -1 - 10 = -11$, and the equation of the line is: $y = 5x - 11$.

Finding Midpoint

☑ The middle of a line segment is its midpoint.

☑ The Midpoint of two endpoints A (x_1, y_1) and B (x_2, y_2) can be found using this formula: M $(\frac{x_1+x_2}{2}, \frac{y_1+y_2}{2})$

Examples:

1) Find the midpoint of the line segment with the given endpoints. $(1, -3), (3, 7)$

   Solution: Midpoint = $(\frac{x_1+x_2}{2}, \frac{y_1+y_2}{2}) \rightarrow (x_1, y_1) = (1, -3)$ and $(x_2, y_2) = (3, 7)$

   Midpoint = $(\frac{1+3}{2}, \frac{-3+7}{2}) \rightarrow (\frac{4}{2}, \frac{4}{2}) \rightarrow M(2, 2)$

2) Find the midpoint of the line segment with the given endpoints. $(-4, 5), (8, -7)$

   Solution: Midpoint = $(\frac{x_1+x_2}{2}, \frac{y_1+y_2}{2}) \rightarrow (x_1, y_1) = (-4, 5)$ and $(x_2, y_2) = (8, -7)$

   Midpoint = $(\frac{-4+8}{2}, \frac{5-7}{2}) \rightarrow (\frac{4}{2}, \frac{-2}{2}) \rightarrow M(2, -1)$

3) Find the midpoint of the line segment with the given endpoints. $(5, -2), (1, 10)$

   Solution: Midpoint = $(\frac{x_1+x_2}{2}, \frac{y_1+y_2}{2}) \rightarrow (x_1, y_1) = (5, -2)$ and $(x_2, y_2) = (1, 10)$

   Midpoint = $(\frac{5+1}{2}, \frac{-2+10}{2}) \rightarrow (\frac{6}{2}, \frac{8}{2}) \rightarrow M(3, 4)$

4) Find the midpoint of the line segment with the given endpoints. $(2, 3), (12, -9)$

   Solution: Midpoint = $(\frac{x_1+x_2}{2}, \frac{y_1+y_2}{2}) \rightarrow (x_1, y_1) = (2, 3)$ and $(x_2, y_2) = (12, -3)$

   Midpoint = $(\frac{2+12}{2}, \frac{3-9}{2}) \rightarrow (\frac{14}{2}, \frac{-6}{2}) \rightarrow M(7, -3)$

Praxis Core Math Prep 2020-2021

Finding Distance of Two Points

☑ Use following formula to find the distance of two points with the coordinates A (x_1, y_1) and B (x_2, y_2):

$$d = \sqrt{(x_2 - x_1)^2 + (y_2 - y_1)^2}$$

Examples:

1) Find the distance between $(4, 6)$ *and* $(1, 2)$.

   Solution: *Use distance of two points formula:* $d = \sqrt{(x_2 - x_1)^2 + (y_2 - y_1)^2}$

   $(x_1, y_1) = (4, 6)$ and $(x_2, y_2) = (1, 2)$. *Then:* $d = \sqrt{(x_2 - x_1)^2 + (y_2 - y_1)^2} \rightarrow$

   $$d = \sqrt{(1 - (4))^2 + (2 - 6)^2} = \sqrt{(-3)^2 + (-4)^2} = \sqrt{9 + 16} = \sqrt{25} = 5 \rightarrow d = 5$$

2) Find the distance of two points $(-6, -10)$ *and* $(-2, -10)$.

   Solution: *Use distance of two points formula:* $d = \sqrt{(x_2 - x_1)^2 + (y_2 - y_1)^2}$

   $(x_1, y_1) = (-6, -10)$, and $(x_2, y_2) = (-2, -10)$

   Then: $d = \sqrt{(x_2 - x_1)^2 + (y_2 - y_1)^2} \rightarrow d = \sqrt{(-2 - (-6))^2 + (-10 - (-10))^2} =$

   $\sqrt{(4)^2 + (0)^2} = \sqrt{16 + 0} = \sqrt{16} = 4$. Then: $d = 4$

3) Find the distance between $(-6, 5)$ *and* $(-2, 2)$.

   Solution: *Use distance of two points formula:* $d = \sqrt{(x_2 - x_1)^2 + (y_2 - y_1)^2}$

   $(x_1, y_1) = (-6, 5)$ and $(x_2, y_2) = (-2, 2)$. *Then:* $d = \sqrt{(x_2 - x_1)^2 + (y_2 - y_1)^2} \rightarrow$

   $$d = \sqrt{(-2 - (-6))^2 + (2 - 5)^2} = \sqrt{(4)^2 + (-3)^2} = \sqrt{16 + 9} = \sqrt{25} = 5$$

Chapter 8: Practices

✎ **Find the slope of each line.**

1) $y = x - 1$
2) $y = -2x + 5$
3) $y = 2x - 1$

4) Line through $(-2, 4)$ and $(6, 0)$
5) Line through $(-3, 5)$ and $(-2, 8)$
6) Line through $(-3, -1)$ and $(0, -4)$

✎ **Sketch the graph of each line. (Using Slope–Intercept Form)**

7) $y = x + 2$

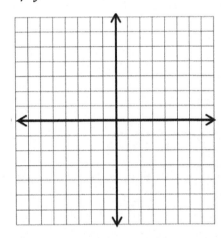

8) $y = 2x - 3$

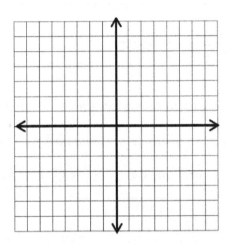

✎ **Solve.**

9) What is the equation of a line with slope 4 and intercept 12? _____

10) What is the equation of a line with slope 4 and passes through point $(4, 2)$?

_____

11) What is the equation of a line with slope -2 and passes through point $(-2, 4)$?

_____

12) The slope of a line is -3 and it passes through point $(-1, 5)$. What is the equation of the line? _____

13) The slope of a line is 3 and it passes through point $(-1, 4)$. What is the equation of the line? _____

Praxis Core Math Prep 2020-2021

✎ *Sketch the graph of each linear inequality. (Graphing Linear Inequalities)*

15) $y > 3x - 1$

16) $y < -x + 4$

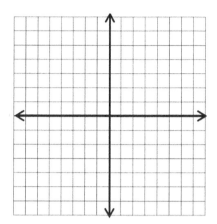

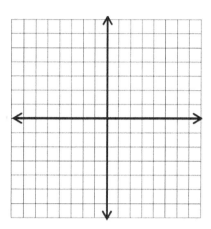

✎ *Find the midpoint of the line segment with the given endpoints.*

17) $(2, 5), (-2, 7)$

18) $(-3, 6), (5, 2)$

19) $(9, -7), (-6, 5)$

20) $(14, -8), (-4, -2)$

21) $(-11, 2), (3, 8)$

22) $(7, 10), (1, -6)$

✎ *Find the distance between each pair of points.*

23) $(3, 10), (-2, -2)$

24) $(1, 6), (4, 10)$

25) $(-2, -1), (-8, 7)$

26) $(8, -2), (5, -6)$

27) $(4, -3), (-5, 9)$

28) $(0, 6), (3, 2)$

Answers – Chapter 8

Find the slope of the line through each pair of points.

1) 1
2) −2
3) 2

4) $-\frac{1}{2}$
5) 3
6) −1

Sketch the graph of each line. (Using Slope–Intercept Form)

7) $y = x + 2$

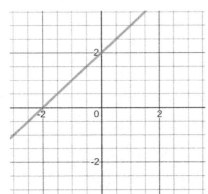

8) $y = 2x - 3$

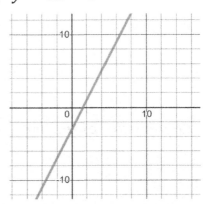

Write the equation of the line through the given points.

9) $y = 4x + 12$
10) $y = 4x - 14$
11) $y = -2x + 8$
12) $y = -3x + 2$
13) $y = 3x + 7$

Sketch the graph of each linear inequality. (Graphing Linear Inequalities)

15) $y > 3x - 1$

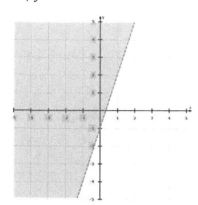

16) $y < -x + 4$

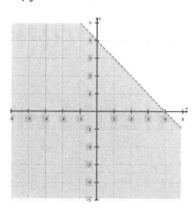

Find the midpoint of the line segment with the given endpoints.

17) $(0, 6)$

18) $(1, 4)$

19) $(1.5, -1)$

20) $(5, -5)$

21) $(-4, 5)$

22) $(4, 2)$

Find the distance between each pair of points.

23) 13

24) 5

25) 10

26) 5

27) 15

28) 5

Chapter 9:

Exponents and Variables

Math Topics that you'll learn in this Chapter:

- ✓ Multiplication Property of Exponents

- ✓ Division Property of Exponents

- ✓ Powers of Products and Quotients

- ✓ Zero and Negative Exponents

- ✓ Negative Exponents and Negative Bases

- ✓ Scientific Notation

- ✓ Radicals

Multiplication Property of Exponents

☑ Exponents are shorthand for repeated multiplication of the same number by itself. For example, instead of 2×2, we can write 2^2. For $3 \times 3 \times 3 \times 3$, we can write 3^4

☑ In algebra, a variable is a letter used to stand for a number. The most common letters are: $x, y, z, a, b, c, m,$ and n.

☑ Exponent's rules: $x^a \times x^b = x^{a+b}$, $\dfrac{x^a}{x^b} = x^{a-b}$

$$(x^a)^b = x^{a \times b} \qquad (xy)^a = x^a \times y^a \qquad \left(\dfrac{a}{b}\right)^c = \dfrac{a^c}{b^c}$$

Examples:

1) *Multiply.* $4x^3 \times 2x^2$

   Solution: Use Exponent's rules: $x^a \times x^b = x^{a+b} \rightarrow x^3 \times x^2 = x^{3+2} = x^5$

   Then: $4x^3 \times 2x^2 = 8x^5$

2) *Simplify.* $(x^3 y^5)^2$

   Solution: Use Exponent's rules: $(x^a)^b = x^{a \times b}$. Then: $(x^3 y^5)^2 = x^{3 \times 2} y^{5 \times 2} = x^6 y^{10}$

3) *Multiply.* $-2x^5 \times 7x^3$

   Solution: Use Exponent's rules: $x^a \times x^b = x^{a+b} \rightarrow x^5 \times x^3 = x^{5+3} = x^8$

   Then: $-2x^5 \times 7x^3 = -14x^8$

4) *Simplify.* $(x^2 y^4)^3$

   Solution: Use Exponent's rules: $(x^a)^b = x^{a \times b}$. Then: $(x^2 y^4)^3 = x^{2 \times 3} y^{4 \times 3} = x^6 y^{12}$

Division Property of Exponents

☑ Exponents are shorthand for repeated multiplication of the same number by itself. For example, instead of 3×3, we can write 3^2. For $2 \times 2 \times 2$, we can write 2^3

☑ For division of exponents use following formulas:

$$\frac{x^a}{x^b} = x^{a-b}, x \neq 0, \qquad \frac{x^a}{x^b} = \frac{1}{x^{b-a}}, x \neq 0, \qquad \frac{1}{x^b} = x^{-b}$$

Examples:

1) *Simplify.* $\frac{12x^2 y}{4xy^3} =$

   Solution: First cancel the common factor: $4 \to \frac{12x^2 y}{4xy^3} = \frac{3x^2 y}{xy^3}$

   Use Exponent's rules: $\frac{x^a}{x^b} = x^{a-b} \to \frac{x^2}{x} = x^{2-1} = x$ and $\frac{y}{y^3} = \frac{1}{y^{3-1}} = \frac{1}{y^2}$

   Then: $\frac{12x^2 y}{4xy^3} = \frac{3x}{y^2}$

2) *Simplify.* $\frac{18x^6}{2x^3} =$

   Solution: Use Exponent's rules: $\frac{x^a}{x^b} = x^{b-a} \to \frac{x^6}{x^3} = x^{6-3} = x^3$

   Then: $\frac{18x^6}{2x^3} = 9x^3$

3) *Simplify.* $\frac{8x^3 y}{40x^2 y^3} =$

   Solution: First cancel the common factor: $8 \to \frac{8x^3 y}{40x^2 y^3} = \frac{x^3 y}{5x^2 y^3}$

   Use Exponent's rules: $\frac{x^a}{x^b} = x^{a-b} \to \frac{x^3}{x^2} = x^{3-2} = x$

   Then: $\frac{8x^3 y}{40x^2 y^3} = \frac{xy}{5y^3} \to$ now cancel the common factor: $y \to \frac{xy}{5y^3} = \frac{x}{5y^2}$

Powers of Products and Quotients

☑ Exponents are shorthand for repeated multiplication of the same number by itself. For example, instead of $2 \times 2 \times 2$, we can write 2^3. For $3 \times 3 \times 3 \times 3$, we can write 3^4

☑ For any nonzero numbers a and b and any integer x, $(ab)^x = a^x \times b^x$ and $(\frac{a}{b})^c = \frac{a^c}{b^c}$

Examples:

1) *Simplify.* $(6x^2y^4)^2$

Solution: Use Exponent's rules: $(x^a)^b = x^{a \times b}$

$(6x^2y^4)^2 = (6)^2(x^2)^2(y^4)^2 = 36x^{2 \times 2}y^{4 \times 2} = 36x^4y^8$

2) *Simplify.* $(\frac{5x}{2x^2})^2$

Solution: First cancel the common factor: $x \rightarrow (\frac{5x}{2x^2})^2 = (\frac{5}{2x})^2$

Use Exponent's rules: $(\frac{a}{b})^c = \frac{a^c}{b^c}$, Then: $(\frac{5}{2x})^2 = \frac{5^2}{(2x)^2} = \frac{25}{4x^2}$

3) *Simplify.* $(3x^5y^4)^2$

Solution: Use Exponent's rules: $(x^a)^b = x^{a \times b}$

$(3x^5y^4)^2 = (3)^2(x^5)^2(y^4)^2 = 9x^{5 \times 2}y^{4 \times 2} = 9x^{10}y^8$

4) *Simplify.* $(\frac{2x}{3x^2})^2$

Solution: First cancel the common factor: $x \rightarrow (\frac{2x}{3x^2})^2 = (\frac{2}{3x})^2$

Use Exponent's rules: $(\frac{a}{b})^c = \frac{a^c}{b^c}$, Then: $(\frac{2}{3x})^2 = \frac{2^2}{(3x)^2} = \frac{4}{9x^2}$

Zero and Negative Exponents

☑ Zero-Exponent Rule: $a^0 = 1$, this means that anything raised to the zero power is 1. For example: $(5xy)^0 = 1$

☑ A negative exponent simply means that the base is on the wrong side of the fraction line, so you need to flip the base to the other side. For instance, "x^{-2}" (pronounced as "ecks to the minus two") just means "x^2" but underneath, as in $\frac{1}{x^2}$.

Examples:

1) Evaluate. $\left(\frac{2}{3}\right)^{-2} =$

   Solution: Use negative exponent's rule: $\left(\frac{x^a}{x^b}\right)^{-2} = \left(\frac{x^b}{x^a}\right)^2 \rightarrow \left(\frac{2}{3}\right)^{-2} = \left(\frac{3}{2}\right)^2 =$

   Then: $\left(\frac{3}{2}\right)^2 = \frac{3^2}{2^2} = \frac{9}{4}$

2) Evaluate. $\left(\frac{4}{5}\right)^{-3} =$

   Solution: Use negative exponent's rule: $\left(\frac{x^a}{x^b}\right)^{-2} = \left(\frac{x^b}{x^a}\right)^2 \rightarrow \left(\frac{4}{5}\right)^{-3} = \left(\frac{5}{4}\right)^3 =$

   Then: $\left(\frac{5}{4}\right)^3 = \frac{5^3}{4^3} = \frac{125}{64}$

3) Evaluate. $\left(\frac{x}{y}\right)^0 =$

   Solution: Use zero-exponent Rule: $a^0 = 1$
   Then: $\left(\frac{x}{y}\right)^0 = 1$

4) Evaluate. $\left(\frac{5}{6}\right)^{-1} =$

   Solution: Use negative exponent's rule: $\left(\frac{x^a}{x^b}\right)^{-2} = \left(\frac{x^b}{x^a}\right)^2 \rightarrow \left(\frac{5}{6}\right)^{-1} = \left(\frac{6}{5}\right)^1 = \frac{6}{5}$

Negative Exponents and Negative Bases

☑ A negative exponent is the reciprocal of that number with a positive exponent. $(3)^{-2} = \frac{1}{3^2}$

☑ To simplify a negative exponent, make the power positive!

☑ The parenthesis is important! -5^{-2} is not the same as $(-5)^{-2}$

$$- 5^{-2} = -\frac{1}{5^2} \text{ and } (-5)^{-2} = +\frac{1}{5^2}$$

Examples:

1) *Simplify.* $\left(\frac{5a}{6c}\right)^{-2} =$

Solution: Use negative exponent's rule: $\left(\frac{x^a}{x^b}\right)^{-2} = \left(\frac{x^b}{x^a}\right)^2 \to \left(\frac{5a}{6c}\right)^{-2} = \left(\frac{6c}{5a}\right)^2$

Now use exponent's rule: $\left(\frac{a}{b}\right)^c = \frac{a^c}{b^c} \to = \left(\frac{6c}{5a}\right)^2 = \frac{6^2c^2}{5^2a^2}$

Then: $\frac{6^2c^2}{5^2a^2} = \frac{36c^2}{25a^2}$

2) *Simplify.* $\left(\frac{2x}{3yz}\right)^{-3} =$

Solution: Use negative exponent's rule: $\left(\frac{x^a}{x^b}\right)^{-2} = \left(\frac{x^b}{x^a}\right)^2 \to \left(\frac{2x}{3yz}\right)^{-3} = \left(\frac{3yz}{2x}\right)^3$

Now use exponent's rule: $\left(\frac{a}{b}\right)^c = \frac{a^c}{b^c} \to \left(\frac{3yz}{2x}\right)^3 = \frac{3^3y^3z^3}{2^3x^3} = \frac{27y^3z^3}{8x^3}$

3) *Simplify.* $\left(\frac{3a}{2c}\right)^{-2} =$

Solution: Use negative exponent's rule: $\left(\frac{x^a}{x^b}\right)^{-2} = \left(\frac{x^b}{x^a}\right)^2 \to \left(\frac{3a}{2c}\right)^{-2} = \left(\frac{2c}{3a}\right)^2$

Now use exponent's rule: $\left(\frac{a}{b}\right)^c = \frac{a^c}{b^c} \to = \left(\frac{2c}{3a}\right)^2 = \frac{2^2c^2}{3^2a^2}$

Then: $\frac{2^2c^2}{3^2a^2} = \frac{4c^2}{9a^2}$

Scientific Notation

☑ Scientific notation is used to write very big or very small numbers in decimal form.

☑ In scientific notation all numbers are written in the form of: $m \times 10^n$, where m is greater than 1 and less than 10.

☑ To convert a number from scientific notation to standard form, move the decimal point to the left (if the exponent of ten is a negative number), or to the right (if the exponent is positive).

Examples:

1) *Write* 0.00015 *in scientific notation.*

   Solution: First, move the decimal point to the right so that you have a number that is between 1 and 10. That number is 1.5

   Now, determine how many places the decimal moved in step 1 by the power of 10. We moved the decimal point 4 digits to the right. Then: 10^{-4} → When the decimal moved to the right, the exponent is negative. Then: $0.00015 = 1.5 \times 10^{-4}$

2) *Write* $\mathbf{9.5 \times 10^{-5}}$ *in standard notation.*

   Solution: 10^{-5} → When the decimal moved to the right, the exponent is negative. Then: $9.5 \times 10^{-5} = 0.000095$

3) *Write* $\mathbf{0.00012}$ *in scientific notation.*

   Solution: First, move the decimal point to the right so that you have a number that is between 1 and 10. Then: $m = 1.2$

   Now, determine how many places the decimal moved in step 1 by the power of 10. 10^{-4} → Then: $0.00012 = 1.2 \times 10^{-4}$

4) *Write* $\mathbf{8.3 \times 10^5}$ *in standard notation.*

   Solution: 10^{-5} → The exponent is positive 5. Then, move the decimal point to the right five digits. (remember $8.3 = 8.30000$)

   Then: $8.3 \times 10^5 = 830000$

Radicals

☑ If n is a positive integer and x is a real number, then: $\sqrt[n]{x} = x^{\frac{1}{n}}$,

$\sqrt[n]{xy} = x^{\frac{1}{n}} \times y^{\frac{1}{n}}$, $\sqrt[n]{\frac{x}{y}} = \frac{x^{\frac{1}{n}}}{y^{\frac{1}{n}}}$, and $\sqrt[n]{x} \times \sqrt[n]{y} = \sqrt[n]{xy}$

☑ A square root of x is a number r whose square is: $r^2 = x$ (r is a square root of x.

☑ To add and subtract radicals, we need to have the same values under the radical. For example: $\sqrt{3} + \sqrt{3} = 2\sqrt{3}$, $3\sqrt{5} - \sqrt{5} = 2\sqrt{5}$

Examples:

1) *Find the square root of $\sqrt{169}$.*

   Solution: First factor the number: $169 = 13^2$,

   Then: $\sqrt{169} = \sqrt{13^2}$

   Now use radical rule: $\sqrt[n]{a^n} = a$.

   Then: $\sqrt{169} = \sqrt{13^2} = 13$

2) *Evaluate.* $\sqrt{9} \times \sqrt{25} =$

   Solution: Find the values of $\sqrt{9}$ and $\sqrt{25}$.

   Then: $\sqrt{9} \times \sqrt{25} = 3 \times 5 = 15$

3) *Solve.* $7\sqrt{2} + 4\sqrt{2}$.

   Solution: Since we have the same values under the radical, we can add these two radicals: $7\sqrt{2} + 4\sqrt{2} = 11\sqrt{2}$

4) *Evaluate.* $\sqrt{2} \times \sqrt{8} =$

   Solution: Use this radical rule: $\sqrt[n]{x} \times \sqrt[n]{y} = \sqrt[n]{xy} \rightarrow \sqrt{2} \times \sqrt{8} = \sqrt{16}$

   The square root of 16 is 4. Then: $\sqrt{2} \times \sqrt{8} = \sqrt{16} = 4$

Chapter 9: Practices

✍️ *Simplify and write the answer in exponential form.*

1) $3x^3 \times 5xy^2 =$

2) $4x^2y \times 6x^2y^2 =$

3) $8x^3y^2 \times 2x^2y^3 =$

4) $7xy^4 \times 3x^2y =$

5) $6x^4y^5 \times 8x^3y^2 =$

6) $5x^3y^3 \times 8x^3y^3 =$

✍️ *Simplify. (Division Property of Exponents)*

7) $\dfrac{5^5 \times 5^3}{5^9 \times 5} =$

8) $\dfrac{8x}{24^{\,2}} =$

9) $\dfrac{15^{\,4}}{9x^3} =$

10) $\dfrac{36^{\,3}}{54^{\,3}y^2} =$

11) $\dfrac{14^{\,3}}{49x^4y^4} =$

12) $\dfrac{120x^3y^5}{30^{\,2}y^3} =$

✍️ *Simplify. (Powers of Products and Quotients)*

13) $(8x^4y^6)^3 =$

14) $(3x^5y^4)^6 =$

15) $(5x \times 4xy^2)^2 =$

16) $\left(\dfrac{6x}{x^3}\right)^2 =$

17) $\left(\dfrac{2x^3y^5}{6x^4y^2}\right)^2 =$

18) $\left(\dfrac{42^{\,4}y^6}{21x^3y^5}\right)^3 =$

✍️ *Evaluate the following expressions. (Zero and Negative Exponents)*

19) $\left(\dfrac{2}{5}\right)^{-2} =$

20) $\left(\dfrac{1}{2}\right)^{-8} =$

21) $\left(\dfrac{2}{5}\right)^{-3} =$

22) $\left(\dfrac{3}{7}\right)^{-2} =$

23) $\left(\dfrac{5}{6}\right)^{-3} =$

24) $\left(\dfrac{4}{9}\right)^{-2} =$

✍️ *Simplify. (Negative Exponents and Negative Bases)*

25) $16x^{-3}y^{-4} =$

26) $-9x^2y^{-3} =$

27) $12a^{-4}b^2 =$

28) $25a^3b^{-5}c^{-1} =$

29) $\dfrac{18y}{x^2y^{-2}} =$

30) $\dfrac{21a^{-2}b}{-14c^{-4}} =$

✎ *Write each number in scientific notation.*

31) $0.00615 =$ 33) $36,000 =$

32) $0.000048 =$ 34) $82,000,000 =$

✎ *Evaluate.*

35) $\sqrt{7} \times \sqrt{7} = \underline{\hspace{1.5cm}}$ 38) $\sqrt{16} \times \sqrt{64} = \underline{\hspace{1.5cm}}$

36) $\sqrt{36} - \sqrt{9} = \underline{\hspace{1.5cm}}$ 39) $\sqrt{3} \times \sqrt{12} = \underline{\hspace{1.5cm}}$

37) $\sqrt{25} + \sqrt{49} = \underline{\hspace{1.5cm}}$ 40) $2\sqrt{6} + 3\sqrt{6} = \underline{\hspace{1.5cm}}$

Answers – Chapter 9

1) $15x^4y^2$
2) $24x^4y^3$
3) $16x^5y^5$
4) $21x^3y^5$
5) $48x^7y^7$
6) $40x^6y^6$
7) $\dfrac{1}{25}$
8) $\dfrac{1}{3x}$
9) $\dfrac{5}{3}x$
10) $\dfrac{2}{3y^3}$
11) $\dfrac{2}{7x^4y}$
12) $4xy^2$
13) $512x^{12}y^{18}$
14) $729x^{30}y^{24}$
15) $400x^4y^4$
16) $\dfrac{36}{x^4}$
17) $\dfrac{y^6}{9x^2}$
18) $8x^3y^3$
19) $\dfrac{25}{4}$
20) 256
21) $\dfrac{125}{8}$

22) $\dfrac{49}{9}$
23) $\dfrac{216}{125}$
24) $\dfrac{81}{16}$
25) $\dfrac{16}{x^3y^4}$
26) $-\dfrac{9x^2}{y^3}$
27) $\dfrac{12^2}{a^4}$
28) $\dfrac{25a^3}{b^5c}$
29) $\dfrac{18y^3}{x^2}$
30) $-\dfrac{3bc^4}{2a^2}$
31) 6.15×10^{-3}
32) 4.8×10^{-5}
33) 3.6×10^4
34) 8.2×10^7
35) 7
36) 3
37) 12
38) 32
39) 6
40) $5\sqrt{6}$

Chapter 10:

Polynomials

Math Topics that you'll learn in this Chapter:

- ✓ Simplifying Polynomials
- ✓ Adding and Subtracting Polynomials
- ✓ Multiplying Monomials
- ✓ Multiplying and Dividing Monomials
- ✓ Multiplying a Polynomial and a Monomial
- ✓ Multiplying Binomials
- ✓ Factoring Trinomials

Simplifying Polynomials

☑ To simplify Polynomials, find "like" terms. (they have same variables with same power).

☑ Use "FOIL". (First-Out-In-Last) for binomials:

$$(x + a)(x + b) = x^2 + (b + a)x + ab$$

☑ Add or Subtract "like" terms using order of operation.

Examples:

1) Simplify this expression. $x(2x + 5) + 6x =$

   Solution: Use Distributive Property: $x(2x + 5) = 2x^2 + 5x$

   Now, combine like terms: $x(2x + 5) + 6x = 2x^2 + 5x + 6x = 2x^2 + 11x$

2) Simplify this expression. $(x + 2)(x + 3) =$

   Solution: First apply FOIL method: $(a + b)(c + d) = ac + ad + bc + bd$

   $(x + 2)(x + 3) = x^2 + 3x + 2x + 6$

   Now combine like terms: $x^2 + 3x + 2x + 6 = x^2 + 5x + 6$

3) Simplify this expression. $4x(2x - 3) + 6x^2 - 4x =$

   Solution: Use Distributive Property: $4x(2x - 3) = 8x^2 - 12x$

   Then: $4x(2x - 3) + 6x^2 - 4x = 8x^2 - 12x + 6x^2 - 4x$

   Now combine like terms: $8x^2 + 6x^2 = 14x^2$, and $-12x - 4x = -16x$

   The simplified form of the expression: $8x^2 - 12x + 6x^2 - 4x = 14x^2 - 16x$

Adding and Subtracting Polynomials

☑ Adding polynomials is just a matter of combining like terms, with some order of operations considerations thrown in.

☑ Be careful with the minus signs, and don't confuse addition and multiplication!

☑ For subtracting polynomials, sometimes you need to use the Distributive Property: $a(b + c) = ab + ac$, $a(b - c) = ab - ac$

Examples:

1) *Simplify the expressions.* $(x^3 - 3x^4) - (2x^4 - 5x^3) =$

   Solution: First use Distributive Property: $-(2x^4 - 5x^3) = -1(2x^4 - 5x^3) = -2x^4 + 5x^3$

   $\rightarrow (x^3 - 3x^4) - (2x^4 - 5x^3) = x^3 - 3x^4 - 2x^4 + 5x^3$

   Now combine like terms: $x^3 + 5x^3 = 6x^3$ and $-3x^4 - 2x^4 = -5x^4$

   Then: $(x^3 - 3x^4) - (2x^4 - 5x^3) = x^3 - 3x^4 - 2x^4 + 5x^3 = 6x^3 - 5x^4$

   Write the answer in standard form: $6x^3 - 5x^4 = -5x^4 + 6x^3$

2) *Add expressions.* $(2x^3 - 4) + (6x^3 - 2x^2) =$

   Solution: Remove parentheses: $(2x^3 - 4) + (6x^3 - 2x^2) = 2x^3 - 4 + 6x^3 - 2x^2$

   Now combine like terms: $2x^3 - 4 + 6x^3 - 2x^2 = 8x^3 - 2x^2 - 4$

3) *Simplify the expressions.* $(8x^2 - 3x^3) - (2x^2 + 5x^3) =$

   Solution: First use Distributive Property: $-(2x^2 + 5x^3) = -2x^2 - 5x^3 \rightarrow$

   $(8x^2 - 3x^3) - (2x^2 + 5x^3) = 8x^2 - 3x^3 - 2x^2 - 5x^3$

   Now combine like terms and write in standard form: $8x^2 - 3x^3 - 2x^2 - 5x^3 = -8x^3 + 6x^2$

Multiplying Monomials

- ☑ A monomial is a polynomial with just one term: Examples: $2x$ or $7y^2$.
- ☑ When you multiply monomials, first multiply the coefficients (a number placed before and multiplying the variable) and then multiply the variables using multiplication property of exponents.

$$x^a \times x^b = x^{a+b}$$

Examples:

1) *Multiply expressions.* $5xy^4z^2 \times 3x^2y^5z^3$

   Solution: Find same variables and use multiplication property of exponents: $x^a \times x^b = x^{a+b}$

   $x \times x^2 = x^{1+2} = x^3$, $y^4 \times y^5 = y^{4+5} = y^9$ and $z^2 \times z^3 = z^{2+3} = z^5$

   Then, multiply coefficients and variables: $5xy^4z^2 \times 3x^2y^5z^3 = 15x^3y^9z^5$

2) *Multiply expressions.* $-2a^5b^4 \times 8a^3b^4 =$

   Solution: Use multiplication property of exponents: $x^a \times x^b = x^{a+b}$

   $a^5 \times a^3 = a^{5+3} = a^8$ and $b^4 \times b^4 = b^{4+4} = b^8$

   Then: $-2a^5b^4 \times 8a^3b^4 = -16a^8b^8$

3) *Multiply.* $7xy^3z^5 \times 4x^2y^4z^3$

   Solution: Use multiplication property of exponents: $x^a \times x^b = x^{a+b}$

   $x \times x^2 = x^{1+2} = x^3$, $y^3 \times y^4 = y^{3+4} = y^7$ and $z^5 \times z^3 = z^{5+3} = z^8$

   Then: $7xy^3z^5 \times 4x^2y^5z^3 = 28x^3y^7z^8$

4) *Simplify.* $(5a^6b^3)(-9a^7b^2) =$

   Solution: Use multiplication property of exponents: $x^a \times x^b = x^{a+b}$

   $a^6 \times a^7 = a^{6+7} = a^{13}$ and $b^3 \times b^2 = b^{3+2} = b^5$

   Then: $(5a^6b^3) \times (-9a^6b^2) = -45a^{13}b^5$

Praxis Core Math Prep 2020-2021

Multiplying and Dividing Monomials

☑ When you divide or multiply two monomials you need to divide or multiply their coefficients and then divide or multiply their variables.

☑ In case of exponents with the same base, for Division, subtract their powers, for Multiplication, add their powers.

☑ Exponent's Multiplication and Division rules:

$$x^a \times x^b = x^{a+b}, \qquad \frac{x^a}{x^b} = x^{a-b}$$

Examples:

1) *Multiply expressions.* $(-5x^8)(4x^6) =$

   Solution: Use multiplication property of exponents: $x^a \times x^b = x^{a+b} \rightarrow x^8 \times x^6 = x^{14}$

   Then: $(-5x^5)(4x^4) = -20x^{14}$

2) *Divide expressions.* $\frac{14x^5y^4}{2xy^3} =$

   Solution: Use division property of exponents: $\frac{x^a}{x^b} = x^{a-b} \rightarrow \frac{x^5}{x} = x^{5-1} = x^4$ and $\frac{y^4}{y^3} = y$

   Then: $\frac{14x^5y^4}{2xy^3} = 7x^4y$

3) *Divide expressions.* $\frac{56a^8b^3}{8ab^3}$

   Solution: Use division property of exponents: $\frac{x^a}{x^b} = x^{a-b} \rightarrow \frac{a^8}{a} = a^{8-1} = a^7$ and $\frac{b^3}{b^3} = 1$

   Then: $\frac{56a^8b^3}{8ab^3} = 7a^7$

Multiplying a Polynomial and a Monomial

☑ When multiplying monomials, use the product rule for exponents.

$$x^a \times x^b = x^{a+b}$$

☑ When multiplying a monomial by a polynomial, use the distributive property.

$$a \times (b + c) = a \times b + a \times c = ab + ac$$
$$a \times (b - c) = a \times b - a \times c = ab - ac$$

Examples:

1) *Multiply expressions.* $5x(3x - 2)$

   Solution: Use Distributive Property: $5x(3x - 2) = 5x \times 3x - 5x \times (-2) = 15x^2 - 10x$

2) *Multiply expressions.* $x(2x^2 + 3y^2)$

   Solution: Use Distributive Property: $x(2x^2 + 3y^2) = x \times 2x^2 + x \times 3y^2 = 2x^3 + 3xy^2$

3) *Multiply.* $-4x(-5x^2 + 3x - 6)$

   Solution: Use Distributive Property:

   $-4x(-5x^2 + 3x - 6) = (-4x)(-5x^2) + (-4x) \times (3x) + (-4x) \times (-6) =$

   Now, simplify: $(-4x)(-5x^2) + (-4x) \times (3x) + (-4x) \times (-6) = 20x^3 - 12x^2 + 24x$

Multiplying Binomials

✓ A binomial is a polynomial that is the sum or the difference of two terms, each of which is a monomial.

✓ To multiply two binomials, use "FOIL" method. (First–Out–In–Last)

$$(x + a)(x + b) = x \times x + x \times b + a \times x + a \times b = x^2 + bx + ax + ab$$

Examples:

1) *Multiply Binomials.* $(x + 2)(x - 4) =$

   Solution: Use "FOIL". (First–Out–In–Last): $(x + 2)(x - 4) = x^2 - 4x + 2x - 8$

   Then combine like terms: $x^2 - 4x + 2x - 8 = x^2 - 2x - 8$

2) *Multiply.* $(x - 5)(x - 2) =$

   Solution: Use "FOIL". (First–Out–In–Last): $(x - 5)(x - 2) = x^2 - 2x - 5x + 10$

   Then simplify: $x^2 - 2x - 5x + 10 = x^2 - 7x + 10$

3) *Multiply.* $(x - 3)(x + 6) =$

   Solution: Use "FOIL". (First–Out–In–Last): $(x - 3)(x + 6) = x^2 + 6x - 3x - 18$

   Then simplify: $x^2 + 6x - 3x - 18 = x^2 + 3x - 18$

4) *Multiply Binomials.* $(x + 8)(x + 4) =$

   Solution: Use "FOIL". (First–Out–In–Last): $(x + 8)(x + 4) = x^2 + 4x + 8x + 32$

   Then combine like terms: $x^2 + 4x + 8x + 32 = x^2 + 12x + 32$

Factoring Trinomials

To factor trinomials, you can use following methods:

☑ "FOIL": $(x + a)(x + b) = x^2 + (b + a)x + ab$

☑ "Difference of Squares":

$$a^2 - b^2 = (a + b)(a - b)$$
$$a^2 + 2ab + b^2 = (a + b)(a + b)$$
$$a^2 - 2ab + b^2 = (a - b)(a - b)$$

☑ "Reverse FOIL": $x^2 + (b + a)x + ab = (x + a)(x + b)$

Examples:

1) **Factor this trinomial.** $x^2 - 2x - 8$

   Solution: Break the expression into groups. You need to find two numbers that their product is -8 and their sum is -2. (remember "Reverse FOIL": $x^2 + (b + a)x + ab = (x + a)(x + b)$). Those two numbers are 2 and -4. Then:

   $x^2 - 2x - 8 = (x^2 + 2x) + (-4x - 8)$

   Now factor out x from $x^2 + 2x : x(x + 2)$, and factor out -4 from $-4x - 8$: $-4(x + 2)$

   Then: $(x^2 + 2x) + (-4x - 8) = x(x + 2) - 4(x + 2)$

   Now factor out like term: $(x + 2)$. Then: $(x + 2)(x - 4)$

2) **Factor this trinomial.** $x^2 - 2x - 24$

   Solution: Break the expression into groups: $(x^2 + 4x) + (-6x - 24)$

   Now factor out x from $x^2 + 4x : x(x + 4)$, and factor out -6 from $-6x - 24$: $-6(x + 4)$

   Then: $(x + 4) - 6(x + 4)$, now factor out like term:

   $(x = 4) \rightarrow x(x + 4) - 6(x + 4) = (x + 4)(x - 6)$

Praxis Core Math Prep 2020-2021

Chapter 10: Practices

✎ *Simplify each polynomial.*

1) $4(3x + 5) =$

2) $8(6x - 1) =$

3) $2x(7x + 4) + 2x =$

4) $5x(6x + 2) - 4x =$

5) $7x(3x - 6) + x^2 - 2 =$

6) $3x^2 - 5 - 9x(4x + 1) =$

✎ *Add or subtract polynomials.*

7) $(6x^2 + 8) + (2x^2 - 4) =$

8) $(x^2 - 5x) - (3x^2 + 2x) =$

9) $(9x^3 - 4x^2) + (x^3 - 3x^2) =$

10) $(7x^3 - 3x) - (6x^3 - 5x) =$

11) $(12x^3 + x^2) + (2x^2 - 10) =$

12) $(4x^3 - 15) - (3x^3 - 7x^2) =$

✎ *Simplify each expression. (Multiplying Monomials)*

13) $5x^3 \times 6x^4 =$

14) $-4a^2b \times 3ab^2 =$

15) $(-7x^2yz) \times (-3xy^3z^2) =$

16) $9u^4t^2 \times (-4ut) =$

17) $12x^3z \times 3xy^2 =$

18) $-8a^2bc \times a^3b^2 =$

✎ *Simplify each expression. (Multiplying and Dividing Monomials)*

19) $(4x^3y^4)(12x^5y^2) =$

20) $(5x^4y^2)(8x^6y^5) =$

21) $(16x^7y^9)(3x^6y^4) =$

22) $\frac{36\ ^5y^3}{9x^2y} =$

23) $\frac{98\ ^{12}y^{10}}{7x^9y^7} =$

24) $\frac{225x^9y^{13}}{15x^6y^9} =$

✎ Find each product. (Multiplying a Polynomial and a Monomial)

25) $4x(6x - y) =$

26) $7x(3x + 5y) =$

27) $5x(x - 8y) =$

28) $x(3x^2 + 2x - 6) =$

29) $5x(-x^2 + 7x + 4) =$

30) $6x(6x^2 - 3x - 12) =$

✎ Find each product. (Multiplying Binomials)

31) $(x - 3)(x + 3) =$

32) $(x - 5)(x - 4) =$

33) $(x + 6)(x + 3) =$

34) $(x - 7)(x + 8) =$

35) $(x + 2)(x - 9) =$

36) $(x - 15)(x + 3) =$

✎ Factor each trinomial.

37) $x^2 + 4x - 12 =$

38) $x^2 + x - 20 =$

39) $x^2 + 3x - 108 =$

40) $x^2 + 12x + 32 =$

41) $x^2 - 14x + 48 =$

42) $x^2 + 2x - 35 =$

Answers – Chapter 10

1) $12x + 20$
2) $48x - 8$
3) $14x^2 + 10x$

4) $30x^2 + 6x$
5) $22x^2 - 42x - 2$
6) $-33x^2 - 9x - 5$

7) $8x^2 + 4$
8) $-2x^2 - 7x$
9) $10x^3 - 7x^2$

10) $x^3 + 2x$
11) $12x^3 + 3x^2 - 10$
12) $x^3 + 7x^2 - 15$

13) $30x^7$
14) $-12a^3b^3$
15) $21x^3y^4z^3$

16) $-36u^5t^3$
17) $36x^4y^2z$
18) $-8a^5b^3c$

19) $48x^8y^6$
20) $40x^{10}y^7$
21) $48x^{13}y^{13}$
22) $4x^3y^2$

23) $14x^3y^3$

24) $15x^3y^4$

25) $24x^2 - 4xy$
26) $21x^2 + 35xy$
27) $5x^2 - 40xy$

28) $3x^3 + 2x^2 - 6x$
29) $-5x^3 + 35x^2 + 20x$
30) $36x^3 - 18x^2 - 72x$

31) $x^2 - 9$
32) $x^2 - 9x + 20$
33) $x^2 + 9x + 18$

34) $x^2 + x - 56$
35) $x^2 - 7x - 18$
36) $x^2 - 12x - 45$

37) $(x - 2)(x + 6)$
38) $(x + 5)(x - 4)$
39) $(x + 12)(x - 9)$

40) $(x + 8)(x + 4)$
41) $(x - 6)(x - 8)$
42) $(x + 7)(x - 5)$

Chapter 11:

Geometry and Solid Figures

Math Topics that you'll learn in this Chapter:

- ✓ The Pythagorean Theorem
- ✓ Triangles
- ✓ Polygons
- ✓ Circles
- ✓ Trapezoids
- ✓ Cubes
- ✓ Rectangle Prisms
- ✓ Cylinder

The Pythagorean Theorem

☑ You can use the Pythagorean Theorem to find a missing side in a right triangle.

☑ In any right triangle: $a^2 + b^2 = c^2$

Examples:

1) Right triangle ABC (not shown) has two legs of lengths 6 cm (AB) and 8 cm (AC). What is the length of the hypotenuse of the triangle (side BC)?

   Solution: Use Pythagorean Theorem: $a^2 + b^2 = c^2$, $a = 6$, and $b = 8$

   Then: $a^2 + b^2 = c^2 \rightarrow 6^2 + 8^2 = c^2 \rightarrow 36 + 64 = c^2 \rightarrow 100 = c^2 \rightarrow c = \sqrt{100} = 10$

   The length of the hypotenuse is 10 cm.

2) Find the hypotenuse of the following triangle.

   Solution: Use Pythagorean Theorem: $a^2 + b^2 = c^2$

   Then: $a^2 + b^2 = c^2 \rightarrow 12^2 + 5^2 = c^2 \rightarrow 144 + 25 = c^2$

   $c^2 = 169 \rightarrow c = \sqrt{169} = 13$

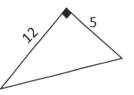

3) Find the length of the missing side in the following triangle.

   Solution: Use Pythagorean Theorem: $a^2 + b^2 = c^2$

   Then: $a^2 + b^2 = c^2 \rightarrow 3^2 + b^2 = 5^2 \rightarrow 9 + b^2 = 25 \rightarrow$

   $b^2 = 25 - 9 \rightarrow b^2 = 16 \rightarrow b = \sqrt{16} = 4$

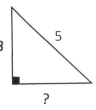

Triangles

☑ In any triangle the sum of all angles is 180 degrees.

☑ Area of a triangle $= \frac{1}{2}(base \times height)$

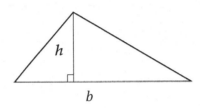

Examples:

What is the area of following triangles?

1)

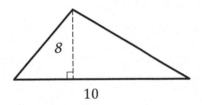

Solution:
Use the area formula: Area $= \frac{1}{2}(base \times height)$
$base = 10$ and $height = 8$
Area $= \frac{1}{2}(10 \times 8) = \frac{1}{2}(80) = 40$

2)

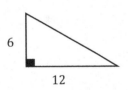

Solution:
Use the area formula: Area $= \frac{1}{2}(base \times height)$
$base = 12$ and $height = 6$
Area $= \frac{1}{2}(12 \times 6) = \frac{72}{2} = 36$

3) What is the missing angle in the following triangle?

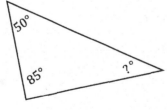

Solution:
In any triangle the sum of all angles is 180 degrees.
Let x be the missing angle. Then: $50 + 85 + x = 180$
$\rightarrow 135 + x = 180 \rightarrow x = 180 - 135 = 45$
The missing angle is 45 degrees.

Polygons

☑ Perimeter of a square

$= 4 \times side = 4s$

 s

☑ Perimeter of a rectangle

$= 2(width + length)$

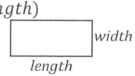

☑ Perimeter of trapezoid

$= a + b + c + d$

☑ Perimeter of a regular hexagon $= 6a$

☑ Perimeter of a parallelogram $= 2(l + w)$

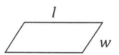

Examples:

1) Find the perimeter of following regular hexagon.

   Solution: Since the hexagon is regular, all sides are equal.

   Then: Perimeter of Hexagon $= 6 \times (one\ side)$

   Perimeter of Hexagon $= 6 \times (one\ side) = 6 \times 4 = 24\ m$

   4 m

2) Find the perimeter of following trapezoid.

   Solution: Perimeter of a trapezoid $= a + b + c + d$

   Perimeter of the trapezoid $= 5 + 6 + 6 + 8 = 25\ ft$

Circles

☑ In a circle, variable r is usually used for the radius and d for diameter.

☑ *Area of a circle* $= \pi r^2$ (π is about 3.14)

☑ *Circumference of a circle* $= 2\pi r$

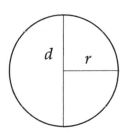

Examples:

1) Find the area of the following circle.

   Solution:

   Use area formula: $Area = \pi r^2$

   $r = 8\ in \rightarrow Area = \pi(8)^2 = 64\pi, \pi = 3.14$

   Then: $Area = 64 \times 3.14 = 200.96\ in^2$

2) Find the Circumference of the following circle.

   Solution:

   Use Circumference formula: $Circumference = 2\pi r$

   $r = 5\ cm \rightarrow Circumference = 2\pi(5) = 10\pi$

   $\pi = 3.14$ ***Then:*** $Circumference = 10 \times 3.14 = 31.4\ cm$

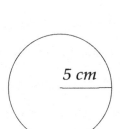

3) Find the area of the circle.

   Solution:

   Use area formula: $Area = \pi r^2$,

   $r = 5\ in$ then: $Area = \pi(5)^2 = 25\pi, \pi = 3.14$

   Then: $Area = 25 \times 3.14 = 78.5$

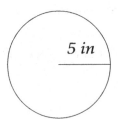

Trapezoids

☑ A quadrilateral with at least one pair of parallel sides is a trapezoid.

☑ Area of a trapezoid $= \frac{1}{2}h(b_1 + b_2)$

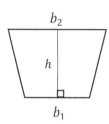

Examples:

1) Calculate the area of the following trapezoid.

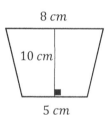

Solution:

Use area formula: $A = \frac{1}{2}h(b_1 + b_2)$

$b_1 = 5 \, cm$, $b_2 = 8 \, cm$ and $h = 10 \, cm$

Then: $A = \frac{1}{2}(10)(8 + 5) = 5(13) = 65 \, cm^2$

2) Calculate the area of the following trapezoid.

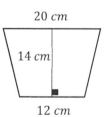

Solution:

Use area formula: $A = \frac{1}{2}h(b_1 + b_2)$

$b_1 = 12 \, cm$, $b_2 = 20 \, cm$ and $h = 14 \, cm$

Then: $A = \frac{1}{2}(14)(12 + 20) = 7(32) = 224 \, cm^2$

Cubes

☑ A cube is a three-dimensional solid object bounded by six square sides.

☑ Volume is the measure of the amount of space inside of a solid figure, like a cube, ball, cylinder or pyramid.

☑ Volume of a cube $= (\textbf{\textit{one side}})^3$

☑ surface area of a cube $= \textbf{6} \times (\textbf{\textit{one side}})^2$

Examples:

1) Find the volume and surface area of the following cube.

   Solution: Use volume formula: $volume = (one\ side)^3$

   Then: $volume = (one\ side)^3 = (2)^3 = 8\ cm^3$

   Use surface area formula: $surface\ area\ of\ cube: 6(one\ side)^2 =$
   $$6(2)^2 = 6(4) = 24\ cm^2$$

   2 cm

2) Find the volume and surface area of the following cube.

   Solution: Use volume formula: $volume = (one\ side)^3$

   Then: $volume = (one\ side)^3 = (5)^3 = 125\ cm^3$

   Use surface area formula:

   $surface\ area\ of\ cube: 6(one\ side)^2 = 6(5)^2 = 6(25) = 150\ cm^2$

   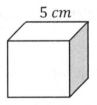
   5 cm

3) Find the volume and surface area of the following cube.

   Solution: Use volume formula: $volume = (one\ side)^3$

   Then: $volume = (one\ side)^3 = (7)^3 = 343\ m^3$

   Use surface area formula:

   $surface\ area\ of\ cube: 6(one\ side)^2 = 6(7)^2 = 6(49) = 294\ m^2$

   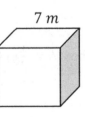
   7 m

Rectangular Prisms

○ A rectangular prism is a solid 3-dimensional object which has six rectangular faces.

○ Volume of a Rectangular prism = **Length × Width × Height**

$Volume = l \times w \times h$

$Surface\ area = 2 \times (wh + lw + lh)$

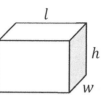

Examples:

1) Find the volume and surface area of the following rectangular prism.

Solution:

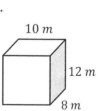

Use volume formula: $Volume = l \times w \times h$

Then: $Volume = 8 \times 6 \times 10 = 480\ m^3$

Use surface area formula: $Surface\ area = 2 \times (wh + lw + lh)$

Then: $Surface\ area = 2 \times \big((6 \times 10) + (8 \times 6) + (8 \times 10)\big)$

$\qquad\qquad = 2 \times (60 + 48 + 80) = 2 \times (188) = 376\ m^2$

2) Find the volume and surface area of rectangular prism.

Solution:

Use volume formula: $Volume = l \times w \times h$

Then: $Volume = 10 \times 8 \times 12 = 960\ m^3$

Use surface area formula: $Surface\ area = 2 \times (wh + lw + lh)$

Then: $Surface\ area = 2 \times \big((8 \times 12) + (10 \times 8) + (10 \times 12)\big)$

$\qquad\qquad = 2 \times (96 + 80 + 120) = 2 \times (296) = 592\ m^2$

Cylinder

☑ A cylinder is a solid geometric figure with straight parallel sides and a circular or oval cross section.

☑ *Volume of a Cylinder* $= \pi (radius)^2 \times height$, $\pi \approx 3.14$

☑ *Surface area of a cylinder* $= 2\pi r^2 + 2\pi rh$

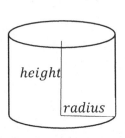

Examples:

1) *Find the volume and Surface area of the follow Cylinder.*

Solution:

Use volume formula: $Volume = \pi (radius)^2 \times height$
Then: $Volume = \pi (3)^2 \times 8 = 9\pi \times 8 = 72\pi$
$\pi = 3.14$ **then:** $Volume = 72\pi = 72 \times 3.14 = 226.08 \ cm^3$
Use surface area formula: $Surface\ area = 2\pi r^2 + 2\pi rh$
Then: $2\pi(3)^2 + 2\pi(3)(8) = 2\pi(9) + 2\pi(24) = 18\pi + 48\pi = 66\pi$
$\pi = 3.14$ Then: $Surface\ area = 66 \times 3.14 = 207.24 \ cm^2$

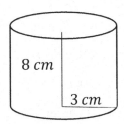

2) *Find the volume and Surface area of the follow Cylinder.*

Solution:

Use volume formula: $Volume = \pi (radius)^2 \times height$
Then: $Volume = \pi (2)^2 \times 6 = \pi 4 \times 6 = 24\pi$
$\pi = 3.14$ **then:** $Volume = 24\pi = 75.36 \ cm^3$
Use surface area formula: $Surface\ area = 2\pi r^2 + 2\pi rh$
Then: $= 2\pi(2)^2 + 2\pi(2)(6) = 2\pi(4) + 2\pi(12) = 8\pi + 24\pi = 32\pi$
$\pi = 3.14$ **then:** $Surface\ area = 32 \times 3.14 = 100.48 \ cm^2$

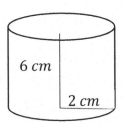

Chapter 11: Practices

✏️ *Find the missing side?*

1)

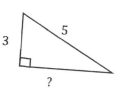

2)

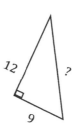

3)

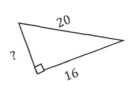

4)

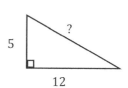

✏️ *Find the measure of the unknown angle in each triangle.*

5)

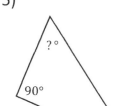

6)

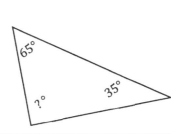

7)

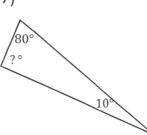

8)

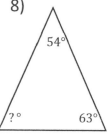

✏️ *Find area of each triangle.*

9)

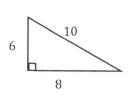

10)

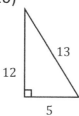

11)

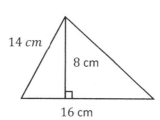

12)

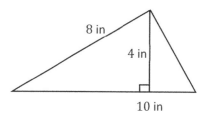

✏️ *Find the perimeter of each shape.*

13)

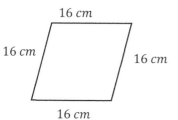

14)

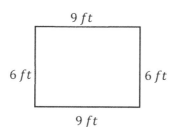

15)

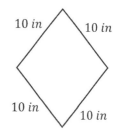

16)

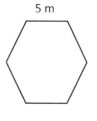

✎ **Complete the table below.** ($\pi = 3.14$)

17)

	Radius	Diameter	Circumference	Area
Circle 1	3 inches	6 inches	18.84 inches	28.26 square inches
Circle 2			43.96 meters	
Circle 3		8 ft		
Circle 4				78.5 square miles

✎ **Find the area of each trapezoid.**

18)

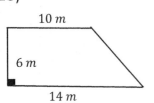

19)

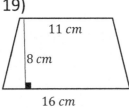

20)

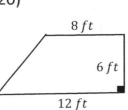

21)

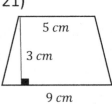

✎ **Find the volume of each cube.**

22)

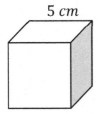

23)

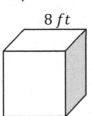

24)

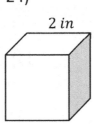

25)

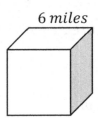

✎ **Find the volume of each Rectangular Prism.**

26)

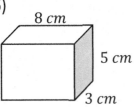

27)

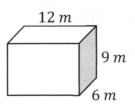

28)

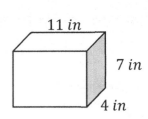

✎ *Find the volume of each Cylinder. Round your answer to the nearest tenth.* ($\pi = 3.14$)

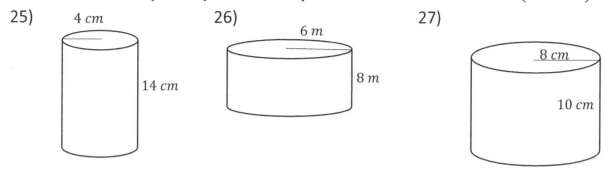

25)

4 cm

14 cm

26)

6 m

8 m

27)

8 cm

10 cm

Answers – Chapter 11

1) 4

2) 15

3) 12

4) 13

5) 60°

6) 80°

7) 90°

8) 63°

9) 24 *square unites*

10) 30 *square unites*

11) 64 cm^2

12) 20 in^2

13) 64 cm

14) 30 ft

15) 40 in

16) 30 m

17)

	Radius	Diameter	Circumference	Area
Circle 1	3 *inches*	6 *inches*	18.84 *inches*	28.26 *square inches*
Circle 2	7 *meters*	14 *meters*	43.96 *meters*	153.86 *square meters*
Circle 3	4 *ft*	8 *ft*	25.12 *ft*	50.24 *square ft*
Circle 4	5 *miles*	10 *miles*	31.4 *miles*	78.5 *square miles*

18) 72 m^2

19) 108 cm^2

20) 60 ft^2

21) 21 cm^2

22) 125 cm^3

23) 512 ft^3

24) 8 in^3

25) 216 $miles^3$

26) 120 cm^3

27) 648 m^3

28) 308 in^3

29) 703.36 cm^3

30) 904.32 m^3

31) 2,009.6 cm^3

Chapter 12:

Statistics

Math Topics that you'll learn in this Chapter:

- ✓ Mean, Median, Mode, and Range of the Given Data

- ✓ Pie Graph

- ✓ Probability Problems

- ✓ Permutations and Combinations

Mean, Median, Mode, and Range of the Given Data

☑ Mean: $\dfrac{sum\ of\ the\ data}{total\ number\ of\ data\ entires}$

☑ Mode: the value in the list that appears most often

☑ Median: is the middle number of a group of numbers that have been arranged in order by size.

☑ Range: the difference of largest value and smallest value in the list

Examples:

1) What is the mode of these numbers? $4, 5, 7, 5, 7, 4, 0, 4$

   Solution: Mode: the value in the list that appears most often.
   Therefore, the mode is number 4. There are three number 4 in the data.

2) What is the median of these numbers? $5, 10, 14, 9, 16, 19, 6$

   Solution: Write the numbers in order: $5, 6, 9, 10, 14, 16, 19$

   Median is the number in the middle. Therefore, the median is 10.

3) What is the mean of these numbers? $8, 2, 8, 5, 3, 2, 4, 8$

   Solution: Mean: $\dfrac{sum\ of\ the\ data}{total\ number\ of\ data\ entires} = \dfrac{8+2+8+5+3+2+4+8}{8} = 5$

4) What is the range in this list? $4, 9, 13, 8, 15, 18, 5$

   Solution: Range is the difference of largest value and smallest value in the list. The largest value is 18 and the smallest value is 4. Then: $18 - 4 = 14$

Praxis Core Math Prep 2020-2021

Pie Graph

☑ A Pie Chart is a circle chart divided into sectors, each sector represents the relative size of each value.

☑ Pie charts represent a snapshot of how a group is broken down into smaller pieces.

Example:

A library has 820 books that include Mathematics, Physics, Chemistry, English and History. Use following graph to answer the questions.

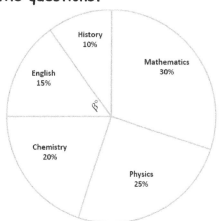

1) What is the number of Mathematics books?

Solution: Number of total books = 820

Percent of Mathematics books = 30% = 0.30

Then, number of Mathematics books:

$$0.30 \times 820 = 246$$

2) What is the number of History books?

Solution: Number of total books = 820

Percent of History books = 10% = 0.10

Then: $0.10 \times 820 = 82$

3) What is the number of Chemistry books?

Solution: Number of total books = 820

Percent of Chemistry books = 20% = 0.20

Then: $0.20 \times 820 = 164$

Probability Problems

☑ Probability is the likelihood of something happening in the future. It is expressed as a number between zero (can never happen) to 1 (will always happen).

☑ Probability can be expressed as a fraction, a decimal, or a percent.

☑ Probability formula: $Probability = \frac{number\ of\ desired\ outcomes}{number\ of\ total\ outcomes}$

Examples:

1) Anita's trick-or-treat bag contains 12 pieces of chocolate, 18 suckers, 18 pieces of gum, 24 pieces of licorice. If she randomly pulls a piece of candy from her bag, what is the probability of her pulling out a piece of sucker?

Solution: Probability $= \frac{number\ of\ desired\ outcomes}{number\ of\ total\ outcomes}$

Probability of ulling out a piece of sucker $= \frac{18}{12+18+18+24} = \frac{18}{72} = \frac{1}{4}$

2) A bag contains 20 balls: four green, five black, eight blue, a brown, a red and one white. If 19 balls are removed from the bag at random, what is the probability that a brown ball has been removed?

Solution: If 19 balls are removed from the bag at random, there will be one ball in the bag. The probability of choosing a brown ball is 1 out of 20. Therefore, the probability of not choosing a brown ball is 19 out of 20 and the probability of having not a brown ball after removing 19 balls is the same.

Permutations and Combinations

☑ Factorials are products, indicated by an exclamation mark. For example, $4! = 4 \times 3 \times 2 \times 1$ (Remember that $0!$ is defined to be equal to 1.)

☑ Permutations: The number of ways to choose a sample of k elements from a set of n distinct objects where order does matter, and replacements are not allowed. For a permutation problem, use this formula:

$$_nP_k = \frac{n!}{(n-k)!}$$

☑ Combination: The number of ways to choose a sample of r elements from a set of n distinct objects where order does not matter, and replacements are not allowed. For a combination problem, use this formula:

$$_nC_r = \frac{n!}{r!\,(n-r)!}$$

Examples:

1) *How many ways can the first and second place be awarded to 8 people?*

    Solution: Since the order matters, (the first and second place are different!) we need to use permutation formula where n is 10 and k is 2. Then: $\frac{n!}{(n-k)!} = \frac{8!}{(8-2)!} = \frac{8!}{6!} = \frac{8 \times 7 \times 6!}{6!}$, remove 6! from both sides of the fraction. Then: $\frac{8 \times 7 \times 6!}{6!} = 8 \times 7 = 56$

2) *How many ways can we pick a team of 2 people from a group of 6?*

    Solution: Since the order doesn't matter, we need to use combination formula where n is 8 and r is 3. Then: $\frac{n!}{r!\,(n-r)!} = \frac{6!}{2!\,(6-2)!} = \frac{6!}{2!\,(4)!} = \frac{6 \times 5 \times 4!}{2!\,(4)!} = \frac{6 \times 5}{2 \times 1} = \frac{30}{2} = 15$

Chapter 12: Practices

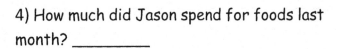 *Find the values of the Given Data.*

1) 6, 12, 1, 1, 5

    Mode: _____   Range: _____

    Mean: _____   Median: _____

2) 5, 8, 3, 7, 4, 3

    Mode: _____   Range: _____

    Mean: _____   Median: _____

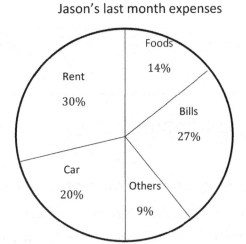

The circle graph below shows all Jason's expenses for last month. Jason spent $864 on his bills last month.

3) How much did Jason spend on his car last month? _____

4) How much did Jason spend for foods last month? _____

Jason's last month expenses

- Foods 14%
- Bills 27%
- Others 9%
- Car 20%
- Rent 30%

✍ *Solve.*

5) Bag A contains 8 red marbles and 6 green marbles. Bag B contains 5 black marbles and 10 orange marbles. What is the probability of selecting a green marble at random from bag A? What is the probability of selecting a black marble at random from Bag B? _____   _____

✍ *Solve.*

6) Susan is baking cookies. She uses sugar, flour, butter, and eggs. How many different orders of ingredients can she try? _____

7) Jason is planning for his vacation. He wants to go to museum, watch a movie, go to the beach, and play volleyball. How many different ways of ordering are there for him? _____

8) In how many ways a team of 10 basketball players can to choose a captain and co-captain? _____

9) How many ways can you give 3 balls to your 8 friends? _____

10) A professor is going to arrange her 8 students in a straight line. In how many ways can she do this? _____

Answers – Chapter 12

1) Mode: 1 , Range: 11, Mean: 5, Median: 5

2) Mode: 3 , Range: 5 , Mean: 5, Median: 4.5

3) $640

4) $448

5) $\frac{3}{7}, \frac{1}{3}$

6) 24

7) 24

8) 90

9) 56

10) 40,320

Chapter 13:

Functions Operations

Math Topics that you'll learn in this Chapter:

✓ Function Notation

✓ Adding and Subtracting Functions

✓ Multiplying and Dividing Functions

✓ Composition of Functions

Function Notation and Evaluation

☑ Functions are mathematical operations that assign unique outputs to given inputs.

☑ Function notation is the way a function is written. It is meant to be a precise way of giving information about the function without a rather lengthy written explanation.

☑ The most popular function notation is $f(x)$ which is read "f of x". Any letter can be used to name a function. for example: $g(x)$, $h(x)$, etc.

☑ To evaluate a function, plug in the input (the given value or expression) for the function's variable (place holder, x).

Examples:

1) Evaluate: $h(n) = n - 2$, find $h(2)$

   Solution: Substitute n with 4: Then: $h(n) = n - 2 \rightarrow h(2) = (2)^2 - 2 \rightarrow h(2) = 4 - 2 = 2$

2) Evaluate: $w(x) = 5x - 1$, find $w(3)$.

   Solution: Substitute x with 3: Then: $w(x) = 5x - 1 \rightarrow w(3) = 5(3) - 1 = 15 - 1 = 14$

3) Evaluate: $f(x) = x^2 - 2$, find $h(2)$.

   Solution: Substitute x with 2: Then: $f(x) = x^2 - 2 \rightarrow f(2) = (2)^2 - 2 = 4 - 2 = 2$

4) Evaluate: $p(x) = 2x^2 - 4$, find $p(3a)$.

   Solution: Substitute x with $3a$: Then: $p(x) = 2x^2 - 4 \rightarrow p(3a) = 2(3a)^2 - 4 \rightarrow$

   $$p(3a) = 2(9a^2) - 4 = 18a^2 - 4$$

Adding and Subtracting Functions

☑ Just like we can add and subtract numbers and expressions, we can add or subtract two functions and simplify or evaluate them. The result is a new function.

☑ For two functions $f(x)$ and $g(x)$, we can create two new functions:
$(f + g)(x) = f(x) + g(x)$ and $(f - g)(x) = f(x) - g(x)$

Examples:

1) $g(x) = a - 1, f(a) = a + 2$, Find: $(g + f)(a)$

   Solution: $(g + f)(a) = g(a) + f(a)$

   Then: $(g + f)(a) = (a - 1) + (a + 2) = 2a + 1$

2) $f(x) = 2x - 2, g(x) = x - 4$, Find: $(f - g)(x)$

   Solution: $(f - g)(x) = f(x) - g(x)$

   Then: $(f - g)(x) = (2x - 2) - (x - 4) = 2x - 2 - x + 4 = x + 2$

3) $g(x) = x^2 - 4, f(x) = 2x + 3$, Find: $(g + f)(x)$

   Solution: $(g + f)(x) = g(x) + f(x)$

   Then: $(g + f)(x) = (x^2 - 4) + (2x + 3) = x^2 + 2x - 1$

4) $f(x) = 2x^2 + 5, g(x) = 3x - 1$, Find: $(f - g)(5)$

   Solution: $(f - g)(x) = f(x) - g(x)$

   Then: $(f - g)(x) = (2x^2 + 5) - (3x - 1) = 2x^2 + 5 - 3x + 1 = 2x^2 - 3x + 6$

   Substitute x with 5: $(g - f)(5) = 2(5)^2 - 3(5) + 6 = 50 - 15 + 6 = 41$

Multiplying and Dividing Functions

☑ Just like we can multiply and divide numbers and expressions, we can multiply and divide two functions and simplify or evaluate them.

☑ For two functions $f(x)$ and $g(x)$, we can create two new functions:

$$(f.g)(x) = f(x).g(x) \text{ and } \left(\frac{f}{g}\right)(x) = \frac{f(x)}{g(x)}$$

Examples:

1) $g(x) = x - 2, f(x) = x + 3$, Find: $(g.f)(x)$

   Solution: $(g.f)(x) = g(x).f(x) = (x-2)(x+3) = x^2 + 3x - 2x - 6$

2) $f(x) = x + 4, h(x) = x - 6$, Find: $\left(\frac{f}{h}\right)(x)$

   Solution: $\left(\frac{f}{h}\right)(x) = \frac{f(x)}{h(x)} = \frac{x+4}{x-6}$

3) $g(x) = x + 5, f(x) = x - 2$, Find: $(g.f)(4)$

   Solution: $(g.f)(x) = g(x).f(x) = (x+5)(x-2) = x^2 - 2x + 5x - 10 = x^2 + 3x - 10$

   Substitute x with 4: $(g.f)(x) = (4)^2 + 3(4) - 10 = 16 + 12 - 10 = 18$

4) $f(x) = 2x + 3, h(x) = x + 8$, Find: $\left(\frac{f}{h}\right)(-1)$

   Solution: $\left(\frac{f}{h}\right)(x) = \frac{f(x)}{h(x)} = \frac{2x+3}{x+8}$

   Substitute x with -1: $\left(\frac{f}{h}\right)(x) = \frac{2x+3}{x+8} = \frac{2(-1)+3}{(-1)+8} = \frac{1}{7}$

Composition of Functions

☑ "Composition of functions" simply means combining two or more functions in a way where the output from one function becomes the input for the next function.

☑ The notation used for composition is: $(fog)(x) = f(g(x))$ and is read "f composed with g of x" or "f of g of x".

Examples:

1) *Using* f(x) = x − 5 *and* g(x) = 2x, *find:* (fog)(x)

   Solution: $(fog)(x) = f(g(x))$. Then: $(fog)(x) = f(g(x)) = f(2x)$

   Now find $f(2x)$ by substituting x with $2x$ in $f(x)$ function. Then: f(x) = x − 5

   $(x \rightarrow 2x) \rightarrow f(2x) = (2x) - 5 = 2x - 5$

2) *Using* f(x) = x + 6 *and* g(x) = x − 2, *find:* (g o f)(−1)

   Solution: $(f \ o \ g)(x) = f(g(x))$. Then: $(g \ o \ f)(x) = g(f(x)) = g(x + 6)$, *now substitute x in* g(x) *by* (x + 6). *Then:* $g(x + 6) = (x + 6) - 2 = x + 6 - 2 = x + 4$

   Substitute x with −1: $(g \ o \ f)(-1) = g(f(x)) = x + 4 = -1 + 4 = 3$

3) *Using* f(x) = 2x − 2 *and* g(x) = 2x, *find:*f(g(5))

   Solution: First find $g(5)$): g(x) = 2x → $g(5) = 2(5) = 10$

   Then: $f(g(5)) = f(10)$. Now, find $f(10)$ by substituting x with 10 in $f(x)$ function.

   Then: $f(g(5)) = f(10) = 2(10) - 2 = 20 - 2 = 18$

Chapter 13: Practices

✏️ *Evaluate each function.*

1) $g(n) = 6n - 3$, find $g(-2)$

   _____

2) $h(x) = -8x + 12$, find $h(3)$

   _____

3) $k(n) = 14 - 3n$, find $k(3)$

   _____

4) $g(x) = 4x - 4$, find $g(-2)$

   _____

5) $k(n) = 8n - 7$, find $k(4)$

   _____

6) $w(n) = -2n + 14$, find $w(5)$

   _____

✏️ *Perform the indicated operation.*

7) $f(x) = x + 6$

   $g(x) = 3x + 3$

   Find $(f - g)(2)$

   _____

8) $g(x) = x - 3$

   $f(x) = -x - 4$

   Find $(g - f)(-2)$

   _____

9) $h(t) = 5t + 4$

   $g(t) = 2t + 2$

   Find $(h + g)(-1)$

   _____

10) $g(a) = 3a - 5$

    $f(a) = a^2 + 6$

    Find $(g + f)(3)$

    _____

11) $g(x) = 4x - 5$

    $h(x) = 6x^2 + 5$

    Find $(g - f)(-2)$

    _____

12) $h(x) = x^2 + 3$

    $g(x) = -4x + 1$

    Find $(h + g)(4)$

    _____

✍ *Perform the indicated operation.*

13) $g(x) = x + 2$

  $f(x) = x + 3$

  Find $(g \cdot f)(4)$

  _____

14) $f(x) = 2x$

  $h(x) = -x + 6$

  Find $(f \cdot h)(-2)$

  _____

15) $g(a) = a + 2$

  $h(a) = 2a - 3$

  Find $(g \cdot h)(5)$

  _____

16) $f(x) = 2x + 4$

  $h(x) = 4x - 2$

  Find $\left(\frac{f}{h}\right)(2)$

  _____

17) $f(x) = a^2 - 2$

  $g(x) = -4 + 3a$

  Find $\left(\frac{f}{g}\right)(2)$

  _____

18) $g(a) = 4a + 6$

  $f(a) = 2a - 8$

  Find $\left(\frac{g}{f}\right)(3)$

  _____

✍ *Using* f(x) = 2x + 5 *and* g(x) = x − 2*, find:*

19) $g\big(f(2)\big) =$ _____

20) $g\big(f(-2)\big) =$ _____

21) $f\big(g(5)\big) =$ _____

22) $f\big(f(4)\big) =$ _____

23) $g\big(f(3)\big) =$ _____

24) $g\big(f(-3)\big) =$ _____

Answers – Chapter 13

1) −15
2) −12
3) 5
4) −12
5) 25
6) 4
7) −1
8) −3
9) −1
10) 19
11) −42
12) 4
13) 42

14) −32
15) 49
16) $\frac{4}{3}$
17) 1
18) −9
19) 7
20) −1
21) 11
22) 31
23) 9
24) −3

Chapter 14:

Quadratic

Math Topics that you'll learn in this Chapter:

✓ Solving a Quadratic Equation

✓ Graphing Quadratic Functions

✓ Solving Quadratic Inequalities

✓ Graphing Quadratic Inequalities

Solving a Quadratic Equations

☑ Write the equation in the form of: $ax^2 + bx + c = 0$

☑ Factorize the quadratic, set each factor equal to zero and solve.

☑ Use quadratic formula if you couldn't factorize the quadratic.

☑ Quadratic formula: $x = \dfrac{-b \pm \sqrt{b^2 - 4ac}}{2a}$

Examples:

Find the solutions of each quadratic.

1) $x^2 + 7x + 12 = 0$

Solution: Factor the quadratic by grouping. We need to find two numbers whose sum is 7 (from $7x$) and whose product is 12. Those numbers are 3 and 4. Then: $x^2 + 7x + 12 = 0 \rightarrow$ $x^2 + 3x + 4x + 12 = 0 \rightarrow (x^2 + 3x) + (4x + 12) = 0$, Now, find common factors: $(x^2 + 3x) = x(x + 3)$ and $(4x + 12) = 3(x + 4)$. We have two expressions $((x^2 + 3x)$ and $(4x + 12))$ and their common factor is $(x + 3)$. Then: $(x^2 + 3x) + (4x + 12) = 0 \rightarrow$ $x(x + 3) + 4(x + 3) = 0 \rightarrow (x + 3)(x + 4) = 0$. The product of two expressions is 0. Then:

$(x + 3) = 0 \rightarrow x = -3$ or $(x + 4) = 0 \rightarrow x = -4$

2) $x^2 + 5x + 6 = 0$

Solution: Use quadratic formula: $x_{1,2} = \dfrac{-b \pm \sqrt{b^2 - 4ac}}{2a}$, $a = 1, b = 5$ and $c = 6$

Then: $= \dfrac{-5 \pm \sqrt{5^2 - 4 \times 1(6)}}{2(1)}$, $x_1 = \dfrac{-5 + \sqrt{5^2 - 4 \times 1(6)}}{2(1)} = -2$, $x_2 = \dfrac{-5 - \sqrt{5^2 - 4 \times 1(6)}}{2(1)} = -3$

3) $x^2 + 6x + 8 = 0$

Solution: Factor: $x^2 + 6x + 8 = 0 \rightarrow (x + 2)(x + 4) = 0 \rightarrow x = -2, \text{ or } x = -4$

Graphing Quadratic Functions

☑ Quadratic functions in vertex form: $y = a(x - h)^2 + k$ where (h, k) is the vertex of the function. The axis of symmetry is $x = h$

☑ Quadratic functions in standard form: $y = ax^2 + bx + c$ where $x = -\frac{b}{2a}$ is the value of x in the vertex of the function.

☑ To graph a quadratic function, first find the vertex, then substitute some values for x and solve for y. (Remember that the graph of a quadratic function is a U-shaped curve and it is called "parabola".)

Examples:

Sketch the graph of $y = (x + 2)^2 - 3$.

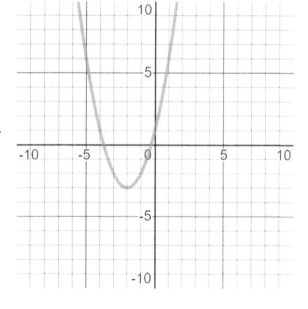

Solution:

Quadratic functions in vertex form: $y = a(x - h)^2 + k$ and (h, k) is the vertex. Then, the vertex of $y = (x + 2)^2 - 3$ is $(-2, -3)$.

Substitute zero for x and solve for y:

$y = (0 + 2)^2 - 3 = 1$.

The y Intercept is $(0,1)$.

Now, you can simply graph the quadratic function.
Notice that quadratic function is a U-shaped curve.

Solving Quadratic Inequalities

☑ A quadratic inequality is one that can be written in the standard form of $ax^2 + bx + c > 0$ (or substitute $<, \leq$, or $\geq$ for $>$).

☑ Solving a quadratic inequality is like solving equations. We need to find the solutions (the zeroes).

☑ To solve quadratic inequalities, first find quadratic equations. Then choose a test value between zeroes. Finally, find interval(s), such as > 0 or < 0.

Examples:

1) **Solve quadratic inequality.** $x^2 + x - 6 > 0$

Solution: First solve $x^2 + x - 6 = 0$ by factoring. Then: $x^2 + x - 6 = 0 \rightarrow$ $(x - 2)(x + 3) = 0$. The product of two expressions is 0. Then: $(x - 2) = 0 \rightarrow x = 2$ or $(x + 3) = 0 \rightarrow x = -3$. Now, choose a value between 2 and -3. Let's choose 0. Then:

$$x = 0 \rightarrow x^2 + x - 6 > 0 \rightarrow (0)^2 + (0) - 6 > 0 \rightarrow -6 > 0$$

-6 is not greater than 0. Therefore, all values between 2 and -3 are NOT the solution of this quadratic inequality. The solution is: $x > 2$ and $x < -3$. To represent the solution, we can use interval notation, in which solution sets are indicated with parentheses or brackets. The solutions $x > 2$ and $x < -3$ represented as: $(\infty, -3) \cup (2, \infty)$

Solution $x \geq 2$ represented as: $[2, \infty)$

2) **Solve quadratic inequality.** $x^2 - 2x - 8 \geq 0$

Solution: First solve: $x^2 - 2x - 8 = 0$, Factor: $x^2 - 2x - 8 = 0 \rightarrow (x - 4)(x + 2) = 0$.

-2 and 4 are the solutions. Choose a point between -2 and 4. Let's choose 0. Then:

$x = 0 \rightarrow x^2 - 2x - 8 \geq 0 \rightarrow (0)^2 - 2(0) - 8 \geq 0 \rightarrow -8 \geq 0$. This is NOT true. So, the solution is: $x \leq -2$ or $x \geq 4$ (using interval notation the solution is: $(\infty, -2] \cup [4, \infty)$

Graphing Quadratic Inequalities

☑ A quadratic inequality is in the form $y > ax^2 + bx + c$ (or substitute $<, \leq,$ or $\geq$ for $>$).

☑ To graph a quadratic inequality, start by graphing the quadratic parabola. Then fill in the region either inside or outside of it, depending on the inequality.

☑ Choose a testing point and check the solution section.

Example:

Sketch the graph of $y > 2x^2$

Solution:

First, graph the quadratic $y = 2x^2$

Since, the inequality sing is $>$, we need to use dash lines.

Now, choose a testing point inside the parabola. Let's choose $(0,2)$.

$y > 2x^2 \rightarrow 2 > 2(0)^2 \rightarrow 2 > 0$

This is true. So, inside the parabola is the solution section.

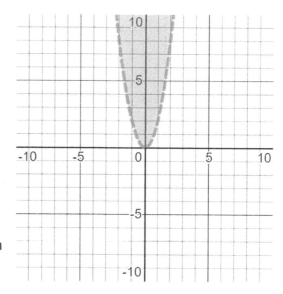

Chapter 14: Practices

✎ *Solve each equation by factoring or using the quadratic formula.*

1) $x^2 - 4x - 32 = 0$

_____

2) $x^2 - 2x - 63 = 0$

_____

3) $x^2 + 17x + 72 = 0$

_____

4) $x^2 + 14x + 48 = 0$

_____

5) $x^2 + 5x - 24 = 0$

_____

6) $x^2 + 15x + 36 = 0$

_____

✎ *Sketch the graph of each function.*

7) $y = (x + 1)^2 - 2$

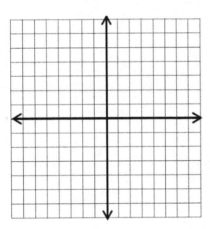

8) $y = (x - 1)^2 + 3$

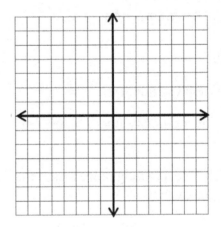

✎ *Solve each quadratic inequality.*

9) $x^2 - 4 < 0$

_____

10) $x^2 - 9 > 0$

_____

11) $x^2 - 5x - 6 < 0$

_____

12) $x^2 + 8x - 20 > 0$

_____

13) $x^2 + 10x - 24 \geq 0$

_____

14) $x^2 + 17x + 72 \leq 0$

_____

✎ *Sketch the graph of each quadratic inequality.*

15) $y < -2x^2$

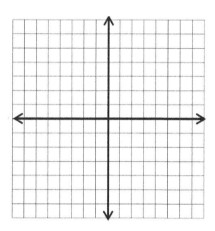

16) $y > 3x^2$

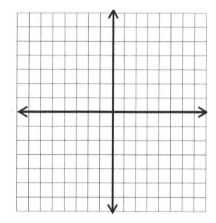

Answers – Chapter 14

1) $x^2 - 4x - 32 = 0$

$x = 8, x = -4$

2) $x^2 - 2x - 63 = 0$

$x = 9, x = -7$

3) $x^2 + 17x + 72 = 0$

$x = -9, x = -8$

7) $y = (x + 1)^2 - 2$

4) $x^2 + 14x + 48 = 0$

$x = -6, x = -8$

5) $x^2 + 5x - 24 = 0$

$x = 3, x = -8$

6) $x^2 + 15x + 36 = 0$

$x = -12, x = -3$

8) $y = (x - 1)^2 + 3$

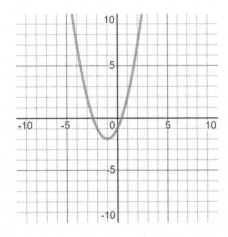

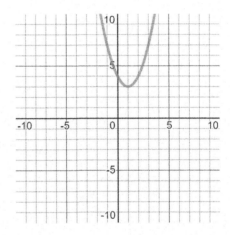

9) $x^2 - 4 < 0$

$-2 < x < 2$

10) $x^2 - 9 > 0$

$-3 < x < 3$

11) $x^2 - 5x - 6 < 0$

$-1 < x < 6$

12) $x^2 + 8x - 20 > 0$

$x < -10 \ or \ x > 2$

13) $x^2 + 10x - 24 \geq 0$

$x \leq -12 \ or \ x \geq 2$

14) $x^2 + 17x + 72 \leq 0$

$-9 \leq x \leq -8$

15) $y < -2x^2$

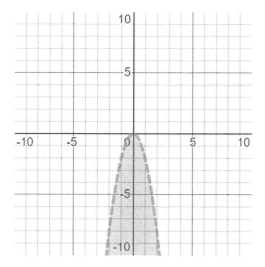

16) $y > 3x^2$

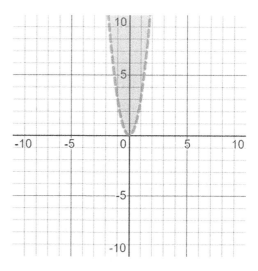

Praxis Core Test Review

The Praxis Core Academic Skills for Educators is a standardized test used for admissions to teacher preparation programs in the United States. In essence, it is a broad and quick assessment of students' academic abilities. The exam was designed and is administered by the Educational Testing Service (ETS) and scoring well on this exam is vital to being accepted for admission into teacher preparation programs.

The Praxis Core test covers three topics.

- Math
- Reading
- Writing

The Praxis Core Math (5733) is comprised of 56 multiple choice and numeric entry questions and test takers have 90 minutes to answer the questions. You will be able to use a basic on-screen calculator on Praxis Core Math test.

Praxis Core Mathematics cover the following topics:

- Number and Quantity (36%)
- Algebra and Functions (20%)
- Geometry (12%)
- Data Interpretation, Statistics and Probability (32%)

In this book, there are two complete Praxis Core Math Tests. Take these tests to see what score you'll be able to receive on a real Praxis Core Math test.

Good luck!

Time to Test

Time to refine your quantitative reasoning skill with a practice test

Take a Praxis Core Math test to simulate the test day experience. After you've finished, score your test using the answer keys.

Before You Start

- You'll need a pencil, a calculator and a timer to take the test.

- For each question, there are five possible answers. Choose which one is best.

- It's okay to guess. There is no penalty for wrong answers.

- After you've finished the test, review the answer key to see where you went wrong.

Good Luck!

Praxis Core Math (5733) Practice Test 1

2020- 2021

Total number of questions: 56

Total time: 90 Minutes

You may use a calculator on this practice test.

(On a real Praxis test, there is an onscreen calculator to use.)

1) In five successive hours, a car traveled $40\ km, 45\ km, 50\ km, 35\ km$ and $55\ km$. In the next five hours, it traveled with an average speed of $65\ km\ per\ hour$. Find the total distance the car traveled in 10 hours.
   A. $425\ km$
   B. $450\ km$
   C. $550\ km$
   D. $600\ km$
   E. $1,000\ km$

2) How long does a 420−miles trip take moving at 65 miles per hour (mph)?
   A. $4\ hours$
   B. $6\ hours\ and\ 24\ minutes$
   C. $8\ hours\ and\ 24\ minutes$
   D. $8\ hours\ and\ 30\ minutes$
   E. $10\ hours\ and\ 30\ minutes$

3) Right triangle ABC has two legs of lengths $5\ cm$ (AB) and $12\ cm$ (AC). What is the length of the third side (BC)?
   A. $4\ cm$
   B. $6\ cm$
   C. $8\ cm$
   D. $13\ cm$
   E. $20\ cm$

Gender	Under 45	45 or older	total
Male	12	6	18
Female	5	7	12
Total	17	13	30

4) The table above shows the distribution of age and gender for 30 employees in a company. If one employee is selected at random, what is the probability that the employee selected be either a female under age 45 or a male age 45 or older?
   A. $\frac{5}{6}$
   B. $\frac{5}{30}$
   C. $\frac{6}{30}$
   D. $\frac{11}{30}$
   E. $\frac{17}{30}$

5) $(7x + 2y)(5x + 2y) = ?$
   A. $2x^2 + 14xy + 2y^2$
   B. $2x^2 + 4xy + 2y^2$
   C. $7x^2 + 14xy + y^2$
   D. $10x^2 + 14xy + 4y$
   E. $35x^2 + 24xy + 4y^2$

6) Which of the following expressions is equivalent to $5x\,(4 + 2y)$?
   A. $x + 10xy$
   B. $5x + 5xy$
   C. $20xy + 2xy$
   D. $20x + 5xy$
   E. $20x + 10xy$

7) If $y = 5ab + 3b^3$, what is y when $a = 2$ and $b = 3$?
   A. 24
   B. 31
   C. 36
   D. 51
   E. 111

8) From the figure, which of the following must be true? (figure not drawn to scale)

   A. $y = z$
   B. $y = 5x$
   C. $y \geq x$
   D. $y + 4x = z$
   E. $y > x$

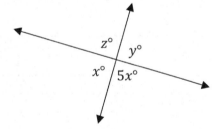

9) The perimeter of the trapezoid below is 64. What is its area?
   A. $252\ cm^2$
   B. $234\ cm^2$
   C. $216\ cm^2$
   D. $154\ cm^2$
   E. $260\ cm^2$

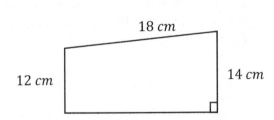

10) Two third of 15 is equal to $\frac{2}{5}$ of what number?
   A. 12
   B. 20
   C. 25
   D. 60
   E. 90

Praxis Core Math Prep 2020-2021

11) The marked price of a computer is D dollar. Its price decreased by 25% in January and later increased by 10% in February. What is the final price of the computer in D dollar?

   A. $0.80 D$
   B. $0.82 D$
   C. $0.90 D$
   D. $1.20 D$
   E. $1.40 D$

12) In the following equation, what is the value of $y - 3x$?

$$\frac{y}{5} = x - \frac{2}{5}x + 2$$

   Write your answer in the box below.

13) What is the value of x in the following equation?

$$\frac{x^2 - 16}{x + 4} + 3(x + 4) = 15$$

   Write your answer in the box below.

14) The length of a rectangle is 3 meters greater than 4 times its width. The perimeter of the rectangle is 36 meters. What is the area of the rectangle in meters?

   Write your answer in the box below.

15) The area of a circle is $49\,\pi$. What is the circumference of the circle?

   A. $7\,\pi$
   B. $14\,\pi$
   C. $32\,\pi$
   D. $64\,\pi$
   E. $124\,\pi$

16) A $50 shirt now selling for $28 is discounted by what percent?
   A. 20%
   B. 44%
   C. 54%
   D. 60%
   E. 80%

17) In 1999, the average worker's income increased $2,000 per year starting from $26,000 annual salary. Which equation represents income greater than average? (I = income, x = number of years after 1999)
   A. $I > 2000\,x + 26000$
   B. $I > -2000\,x + 26000$
   C. $I < -2000\,x + 26000$
   D. $I < 2000\,x - 26000$
   E. $I < 24{,}000\,x + 26000$

18) A boat sails 60 miles south and then 80 miles east. How far is the boat from its start point?
   A. $45\ miles$
   B. $50\ miles$
   C. $60\ miles$
   D. $70\ miles$
   E. $100\ miles$

19) Sophia purchased a sofa for $530.40. The sofa is regularly priced at $631. What was the percent discount Sophia received on the sofa?
   A. 12%
   B. 16%
   C. 20%
   D. 25%
   E. 40%

20) The score of Emma was half as that of Ava and the score of Mia was twice that of Ava. If the score of Mia was 40, what is the score of Emma?
   A. 10
   B. 15
   C. 20
   D. 30
   E. 40

142

21) A bag contains 18 balls: two green, five black, eight blue, a brown, a red and one white. If 17 balls are removed from the bag at random, what is the probability that a brown ball has been removed?

  A. $\dfrac{1}{9}$

  B. $\dfrac{1}{6}$

  C. $\dfrac{16}{18}$

  D. $\dfrac{17}{18}$

  E. $\dfrac{1}{2}$

22) The average of five consecutive numbers is 36. What is the smallest number?

  A. 38
  B. 36
  C. 34
  D. 12
  E. 8

23) The price of a car was $28,000 in 2012. In 2013, the price of that car was $18,200. What was the rate of depreciation of the price of car per year?

  A. 20%
  B. 30%
  C. 35%
  D. 40%
  E. 50%

24) The width of a box is one third of its length. The height of the box is one third of its width. If the length of the box is 36 cm, what is the volume of the box?

  A. 81 cm^3
  B. 162 cm^3
  C. 243 cm^3
  D. 1,728 cm^3
  E. 1,880 cm^3

25) A tree 32 feet tall casts a shadow 12 feet long. Jack is 6 feet tall. How long is Jack's shadow?

  A. 2.25 $feet$
  B. 4 $feet$
  C. 4.25 $feet$
  D. 8 $feet$
  E. 12 $feet$

26) When a number is subtracted from 28 and the difference is divided by that number, the result is 3. What is the value of the number?

   A. 2
   B. 4
   C. 7
   D. 12
   E. 24

27) An angle is equal to one ninth of its supplement. What is the measure of that angle?

   A. 9
   B. 18
   C. 25
   D. 60
   E. 90

28) John traveled 150 km in 6 hours and Alice traveled 140 km in 4 hours. What is the ratio of the average speed of John to average speed of Alice?

   A. $3:2$
   B. $2:3$
   C. $5:7$
   D. $5:6$
   E. $11:16$

29) What is the value of this expression? $[3 \times (-14) - 48] - (-14) + [3 \times 8] \div 2$

   Write your answer in the box below.

   $$\boxed{}$$

30) If $x - 4(x + 2) = -15.5$, what is the value of x?

   Write your answer in the box below.

   $$\boxed{}$$

31) The following graph shows the mark of six students in mathematics. What is the mean (average) of the marks?

A. 15
B. 14.14
C. 14
D. 13.5
E. 11.5

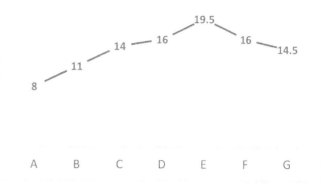

32) A chemical solution contains 6% alcohol. If there is 24 ml of alcohol, what is the volume of the solution?
A. 240 ml
B. 400 ml
C. 600 ml
D. 1,200 ml
E. 2,400 ml

33) The average weight of 18 girls in a class is 56 kg and the average weight of 32 boys in the same class is 62 kg. What is the average weight of all the 50 students in that class?
A. 50
B. 59.84
C. 61.68
D. 61.90
E. 62.20

34) The price of a laptop is decreased by 20% to $360. What is its original price?
A. $320
B. $380
C. $400
D. $450
E. $500

35) A bank is offering 4.5% simple interest on a savings account. If you deposit $9,000, how much interest will you earn in five years?
A. $360
B. $720
C. $2,025
D. $3,600
E. $4,800

36) Multiply and write the product in scientific notation:
$$(2.9 \times 10^6) \times (2.6 \times 10^{-5})$$
    A. 754×100
    B. 75.4×10^6
    C. 75.4×10^{-5}
    D. 7.54×10^{11}
    E. 7.54×10

37) If the height of a right pyramid is $14\ cm$ and its base is a square with side $6\ cm$. What is its volume?
    A. $432\ cm^3$
    B. $3088\ cm^3$
    C. $236\ cm^3$
    D. $172\ cm^3$
    E. $168\ cm^3$

38) 5 less than twice a positive integer is 73. What is the integer?
    A. 39
    B. 41
    C. 42
    D. 44
    E. 50

39) A shirt costing $300 is discounted 15%. After a month, the shirt is discounted another 15%. Which of the following expressions can be used to find the selling price of the shirt?
    A. $(300)(0.70)$
    B. $(300) - 300(0.30)$
    C. $(300)(0.15) - (300)(0.15)$
    D. $(300)(0.85)(0.85)$
    E. $(300)(0.85)(0.85) - (300)(0.15)$

40) Which of the following points lies on the line $2x + 4y = 8$?
    A. $(2,1)$
    B. $(-1,3)$
    C. $(-2,2)$
    D. $(2,2)$
    E. $(2,8)$

41) If $2x + 2y = 2, 3x - y = 7$, which of the following ordered pairs (x, y) satisfies both
   equations?
   A. $(1, 3)$
   B. $(2, 4)$
   C. $(2, -1)$
   D. $(4, -6)$
   E. $(1, -6)$

42) If $f(x) = 3x + 4(x + 1) + 2$ then $f(4x) = ?$
   A. $28x + 6$
   B. $16x - 6$
   C. $25x + 4$
   D. $12x + 3$
   E. $12x - 3$

43) A line in the xy-plane passes through origin and has a slope of $\frac{1}{3}$. Which of the following
   points lies on the line?
   A. $(2,1)$
   B. $(4,1)$
   C. $(9,3)$
   D. $(6,3)$
   E. $(1,3)$

44) Which of the following is equivalent to $(3n^2 + 2n + 6) - (2n^2 - 4)$?
   A. $n + 4n^2$
   B. $n^2 - 3$
   C. $n^2 + 2n + 10$
   D. $n + 2$
   E. $n - 2$

45) Solve for x: $4(x + 1) = 6(x - 4) + 20$
   A. 12
   B. 6.5
   C. 4
   D. 2
   E. 0

46) If $x \neq -4$ and $x \neq 5$, which of the following is equivalent to $\dfrac{1}{\frac{1}{x-5}+\frac{1}{x+4}}$?

A. $\dfrac{(x-5)(x+4)}{(x-5)+(x+4)}$

B. $\dfrac{(x+4)+(x-5)}{(x+4)(x-5)}$

C. $\dfrac{(x+4)(x-5)}{(x+4)-(x+5)}$

D. $\dfrac{(x+4)+(x-5)}{(x+4)-(x-5)}$

E. $\dfrac{(x-4)+(x-5)}{(x+4)-(x-5)}$

$$y < c - x \,,\, y > x + b$$

47) In the xy-plane, if $(0, 0)$ is a solution to the system of inequalities above, which of the following relationships between c and b must be true?

A. $c < b$
B. $c > b$
C. $c = b$
D. $c = b + c$
E. $c = b - x$

48) What is the value of x in the following equation? $3x + 10 = 46$

A. 4
B. 7
C. 10
D. 12
E. 16

49) Calculate $f(5)$ for the following function f.

$$f(x) = x^2 - 3x$$

A. 5

B. 10

C. 15

D. 20

E. 25

148

50) If $\frac{4}{x} = \frac{12}{x-8}$ what is the value of $\frac{x}{2}$?

    A. 1
    B. 3
    C. -2
    D. 2
    E. 0

51) What is the perimeter of a square in centimeters that has an area of $595.36\ cm^2$?

    Write your answer in the box below. (don't write the measurement)

52) A swimming pool holds 2,000 cubic feet of water. The swimming pool is 25 feet long and 10 feet wide. How deep is the swimming pool?

    Write your answer in the box below. (<u>Don't write the measurement</u>)

53) The circle graph below shows all Mr. Green's expenses for last month. If he spent $660 on his car, how much did he spend for his rent?

    A. $700

    B. $740

    C. $810

    D. $910

    E. $960

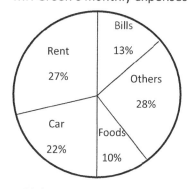

Mr. Green's monthly expenses

54) A function $g(3) = 5$ and $g(5) = 4$. A function $f(5) = 2$ and $f(4) = 6$. What is the value of $f(g(5))$?

    A. 5
    B. 6
    C. 7
    D. 8
    E. 10

55) What is the area of the following equilateral triangle if the side $AB = 12\ cm$?

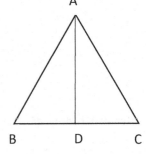

A. $36\sqrt{3}\ cm^2$
B. $18\sqrt{3}\ cm^2$
C. $6\sqrt{3}\ cm^2$
D. $8\ cm^2$
E. $6\ cm^2$

56) If $x \blacksquare y = \sqrt{x^2 + y}$, what is the value of $6 \blacksquare 28$?

A. $\sqrt{168}$
B. 10
C. 8
D. 6
E. 4

End of Praxis Core Math Practice Test 1

Praxis Core Math (5733) Practice Test 2

2020- 2021

Total number of questions: 56

Total time: 90 Minutes

You may use a calculator on this practice test.

(On a real Praxis test, there is an onscreen calculator to use.)

1) The mean of 50 test scores was calculated as 90. But, it turned out that one of the scores was misread as 94 but it was 69. What is the mean?
   A. 85
   B. 87
   C. 89.5
   D. 90.5
   E. 95.5

2) Two dice are thrown simultaneously, what is the probability of getting a sum of 5 or 8?
   A. $\dfrac{1}{3}$
   B. $\dfrac{11}{36}$
   C. $\dfrac{1}{16}$
   D. $\dfrac{1}{4}$
   E. $\dfrac{1}{36}$

3) Which of the following is equal to the expression below?

$$(5x + 2y)(2x - y)$$

   A. $4x^2 - 2y^2$
   B. $2x^2 + 6xy - 2y^2$
   C. $24x^2 + 2xy - 2y^2$
   D. $10x^2 - xy - 2y^2$
   E. $8x^2 + 2xy - 2y^2$

4) What is the product of all possible values of x in the following equation?

$$|x - 10| = 4$$

   A. 3
   B. 7
   C. 13
   D. 84
   E. 100

5) What is the slope of a line that is perpendicular to the line $4x - 2y = 6$?
   A. -2
   B. $-\dfrac{1}{2}$
   C. 4
   D. 12
   E. 14

6) What is the value of the expression $6(x - 2y) + (2 - x)^2$ when $x = 3$ and $= -2$?
   A. -4
   B. 20
   C. 43
   D. 50
   E. 80

7) A swimming pool holds 2,500 cubic feet of water. The swimming pool is 25 feet long and 10 feet wide. How deep is the swimming pool?
   A. $2\ feet$
   B. $4\ feet$
   C. $6\ feet$
   D. $7\ feet$
   E. $10\ feet$

8) Four one – foot rulers can be split among how many users to leave each with $\frac{1}{3}$ of a ruler?
   A. 4
   B. 6
   C. 12
   D. 24
   E. 48

9) What is the area of a square whose diagonal is 4?
   A. 4
   B. 8
   C. 16
   D. 64
   E. 124

10) The average of five numbers is 26. If a sixth number 42 is added, then, what is the new average? (round your answer to the nearest hundredth)
   A. 25
   B. 26.5
   C. 27
   D. 28.66
   E. 36

Questions 11 to 13 are based on the following data

The result of a research shows the number of men and women in four cities of a country.

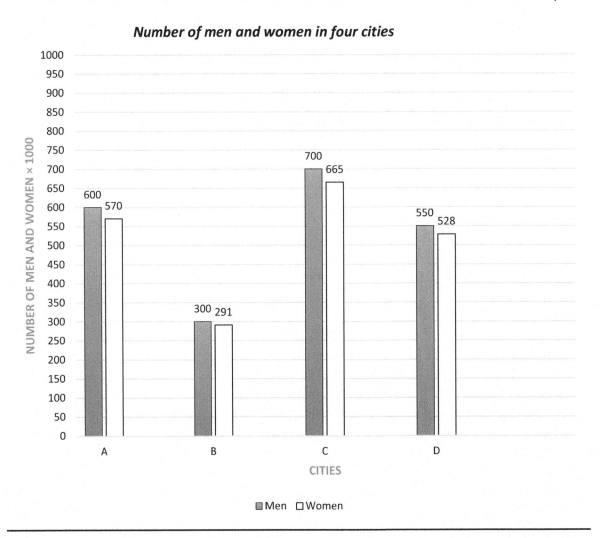

Number of men and women in four cities

11) What's the maximum ratio of the number of women to number of men in each city?

A. 0.98

B. 0.97

C. 0.96

D. 0.95

E. 0.94

12) What's the ratio of the percentage of men in city A to percentage of women in city C?

   A. $\dfrac{10}{9}$

   B. $\dfrac{9}{10}$

   C. 1

   D. $\dfrac{19}{20}$

   E. $\dfrac{20}{19}$

13) How many women should be added to city D to change the ratio of women to men to 1.2?

   A. 130

   B. 129

   C. 132

   D. 131

   E. 133

14) Jason needs an 70% average in his writing class to pass. On his first 4 exams, he earned scores of $68\%, 72\%, 85\%$, and 90%. What is the minimum score Jason can earn on his fifth and final test to pass?

   A. 80%,

   B. 70%

   C. 68%

   D. 54%

   E. 35%

15) What is the value of x in the following equation? $\dfrac{2}{3}x + \dfrac{1}{6} = \dfrac{1}{2}$

   A. 6

   B. $\dfrac{1}{2}$

   C. $\dfrac{1}{3}$

   D. $\dfrac{1}{4}$

   E. $\dfrac{1}{12}$

16) A bank is offering 4.5% simple interest on a savings account. If you deposit $12,000, how much interest will you earn in two years?

   A. $420

   B. $1,080

   C. $4,200

   D. $8,400

   E. $9,600

17) Simplify $7x^2y^3(2x^2y)^3 =$

A. $12x^4y^6$
B. $12x^8y^6$
C. $56x^4y^6$
D. $56x^8y^6$
E. $96x^8y^6$

18) In the diagram below, circle A represents the set of all even numbers, circle B represents the set of all negative numbers, and circle C represents the set of all multiples of 6. Which number could be replaced with y?

A. 6
B. 0
C. −6
D. −10
E. −13

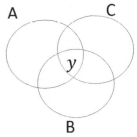

19) Last week 25,000 fans attended a football match. This week three times as many bought tickets, but one sixth of them cancelled their tickets. How many are attending this week?
A. 48,000
B. 54,000
C. 62,500
D. 75,000
E. 84,000

20) What is the perimeter of a square that has an area of 49 square inches?
A. 144 $inches$
B. 64 $inches$
C. 56 $inches$
D. 48 $inches$
E. 28 $inches$

21) If $f(x)=2x^3+5x^2+2x$ and $g(x)=-4$, what is the value of $f(g(x))$?

A. 56
B. 32
C. 24
D. −4
E. −56

Praxis Core Math Prep 2020-2021

22) A cruise line ship left Port A and traveled 50 miles due west and then 120 miles due north. At this point, what is the shortest distance from the cruise to port A?
   A. 70 $miles$
   B. 80 $miles$
   C. 150 $miles$
   D. 230 $miles$
   E. 130 $miles$

23) What is the equivalent temperature of $104°F$ in Celsius?

$$C = \frac{5}{9}(F - 32)$$

   A. 32
   B. 40
   C. 48
   D. 52
   E. 64

24) The perimeter of a rectangular yard is 72 meters. What is its length if its width is twice its length?
   A. 12 $meters$
   B. 18 $meters$
   C. 20 $meters$
   D. 24 $meters$
   E. 36 $meters$

25) The average of 6 numbers is 14. The average of 4 of those numbers is 10. What is the average of the other two numbers?
   A. 10
   B. 12
   C. 14
   D. 22
   E. 24

26) If 150% of a number is 75, then what is the 80% of that number?
   A. 40
   B. 50
   C. 70
   D. 85
   E. 90

27) What is the slope of the line: $4x - 2y = 12$
   A. -1
   B. -2
   C. 1
   D. 1.5
   E. 2

28) In two successive years, the population of a town is increased by 10% and 20%. What percent of the population is increased after two years?
   A. 30%
   B. 32%
   C. 35%
   D. 68%
   E. 70%

29) The area of a circle is 36π. What is the diameter of the circle?
   A. 4
   B. 8
   C. 12
   D. 14
   E. 16

30) If 20% of a number is 4, what is the number?
   A. 4
   B. 8
   C. 10
   D. 20
   E. 25

31) If a tree casts a 26–foot shadow at the same time that a 3 feet yardstick casts a 2–foot shadow, what is the height of the tree?

   A. $24\,ft$
   B. $28\,ft$
   C. $39\,ft$
   D. $48\,ft$
   E. $52\,ft$

32) Jason is 9 miles ahead of Joe running at 6.5 miles per hour and Joe is running at the speed of 8 miles per hour. How long does it take Joe to catch Jason?
   A. $3\,hours$
   B. $4\,hours$
   C. $6\,hours$
   D. $8\,hours$
   E. $10\,hours$

33) 44 students took an exam and 11 of them failed. What percent of the students passed the exam?
   A. 20%
   B. 40%
   C. 60%
   D. 75%
   E. 90%

34) If $f(x) = 2x^3 + 5x^2 + 2x$ and $g(x) = -3$, what is the value of $f(g(x))$?
   A. 36
   B. 32
   C. 24
   D. 15
   E. -15

35) The diagonal of a rectangle is 10 inches long and the height of the rectangle is 6 inches. What is the perimeter of the rectangle?
   A. $10\ inches$
   B. $12\ inches$
   C. $16\ inches$
   D. $18\ inches$
   E. $28\ inches$

36) The perimeter of the trapezoid below is $40\ cm$. What is its area?
   A. $48\ cm^2$
   B. $98\ cm^2$
   C. $140\ cm^2$
   D. $576\ cm^2$
   E. $986\ cm^2$

37) If $f(x) = 2x^3 + 2$ and $(x) = \frac{1}{x}$, what is the value of $f(g(x))$?

   A. $\dfrac{1}{2x^3 + 2}$
   B. $\dfrac{2}{x^3}$
   C. $\dfrac{1}{2x}$
   D. $\dfrac{1}{2x + 2}$
   E. $\dfrac{2}{x^3} + 2$

38) A cruise line ship left Port A and traveled 80 miles due west and then 150 miles due north. At this point, what is the shortest distance from the cruise to port A?

   A. 70 miles

   B. 80 miles

   C. 150 miles

   D. 170 miles

   E. 230 miles

39) If the ratio of $5a$ to $2b$ is $\frac{1}{10}$, what is the ratio of a to b?

   A. 10

   B. 25

   C. $\frac{1}{25}$

   D. $\frac{1}{20}$

   E. $\frac{1}{10}$

40) If $x = 9$, what is the value of y in the following equation? $2y = \frac{2x^2}{3} + 6$

   A. 30

   B. 45

   C. 60

   D. 120

   E. 180

41) If $\frac{x-3}{5} = N$ and $N = 6$, what is the value of x?
   A. 25
   B. 28
   C. 30
   D. 33
   E. 36

42) Which of the following is equal to $b^{\frac{3}{5}}$?

    A. $\sqrt{b^{\frac{5}{3}}}$

    B. $b^{\frac{5}{3}}$

    C. $\sqrt[5]{b^3}$

    D. $\sqrt[3]{b^5}$

    E. $\sqrt[3]{b^{-5}}$

43) On Saturday, Sara read N pages of a book each hour for 3 hours, and Mary read M pages of a book each hour for 4 hours. Which of the following represents the total number of pages of book read by Sara and Mary on Saturday?

    A. $12MN$

    B. $3N + 4M$

    C. $7MN$

    D. $4N + 3M$

    E. $4N - 3M$

44) The average of five numbers is 25. If a sixth number that is greater than 42 is added, then, which of the following could be the new average? (Select one or more answer choices)

    A. 25

    B. 26

    C. 27

    D. 28

    E. 42

45) The diagonal of a rectangle is 10 inches long and the height of the rectangle is 8 inches. What is the perimeter of the rectangle in inches?
Write your answer in the box below.

46) Find the solution (x, y) to the following system of equations?
$$2x + 5y = 11$$
$$4x - 2y = -14$$

   A. $(14, 5)$
   B. $(6, 8)$
   C. $(11, 17)$
   D. $(-2, 3)$
   E. $(2, 3)$

47) Calculate $f(4)$ for the function $f(x) = 3x^2 - 4$.
   A. 44
   B. 40
   C. 38
   D. 30
   E. 20

48) What are the zeroes of the function $f(x) = x^3 + 5x^2 + 6x$?

   A. 0
   B. 2
   C. 0, 2, 3
   D. 0, -2, -3
   E. 0, -2, 3

49) What is the value of the expression? $5 + 8 \times (-2) - [4 + 22 \times 5] \div 6$
   Write your answer in the box below.

50) In the xy-plane, the point $(1, 2)$ and $(-1, 6)$ are on line A. Which of the following points could also be on line A? (Select one or more answer choices)
   A. $(-1, 2)$

   B. $(5, 7)$

   C. $(3, 4)$

   D. $(3, -2)$

   E. $(6, -8)$

51) The function $g(x)$ is defined by a polynomial. Some values of x and $g(x)$ are shown in the table below. Which of the following must be a factor of $g(x)$?

A. x
B. $x - 1$
C. $x - 2$
D. $x + 1$
E. $x + 6$

x	$g(x)$
0	5
1	4
2	0

52) What is the value of $\frac{4b}{c}$ when $\frac{c}{b} = 2$

A. 8
B. 4
C. 2
D. 1
E. 0

53) If $x + 5 = 8$, $2y - 1 = 5$ then $xy + 10 =$

A. 30
B. 24
C. 21
D. 17
E. 15

54) If $\frac{a-b}{b} = \frac{10}{13}$, then which of the following must be true?

A. $\frac{a}{b} = \frac{10}{13}$

B. $\frac{a}{b} = \frac{23}{13}$

C. $\frac{a}{b} = \frac{13}{21}$

D. $\frac{a}{b} = \frac{21}{10}$

E. $\frac{a}{b} = \frac{10}{23}$

55) Which of the following lines is parallel to: $6y - 2x = 24$?

A. $y = \frac{1}{3}x + 2$
B. $y = 3x + 5$
C. $y = x - 2$
D. $y = 2x - 1$
E. $y = -x - 1$

56) Sara orders a box of pen for $3 per box. A tax of 8.5% is added to the cost of the pens before a flat shipping fee of $6 closest out the transaction. Which of the following represents total cost of p boxes of pens in dollars?

A. $1.085(3p) + 6$
B. $6p + 3$
C. $1.085(6p) + 3$
D. $3p + 6$
E. $6p + 6$

End of Praxis Core Math Practice Test 2

Praxis Core Math Practice Tests Answer Keys

Now, it's time to review your results to see where you went wrong and what areas you need to improve.

Praxis Core Math Practice Test 1						Praxis Core Math Practice Test 2					
1	C	21	D	41	C	1	C	21	E	41	D
2	B	22	C	42	A	2	D	22	E	42	C
3	D	23	C	43	C	3	D	23	B	43	B
4	D	24	D	44	C	4	D	24	A	44	D,E
5	E	25	A	45	C	5	B	25	D	45	28
6	E	26	C	46	A	6	C	26	A	46	D
7	E	27	B	47	B	7	E	27	E	47	A
8	D	28	C	48	D	8	C	28	B	48	D
9	E	29	-64	49	B	9	B	29	C	49	-30
10	C	30	2.5	50	C	10	D	30	D	50	D,E
11	B	31	B	51	97.6	11	B	31	C	51	C
12	10	32	B	52	8	12	E	32	C	52	C
13	1.75	33	B	53	C	13	C	33	D	53	B
14	45	34	D	54	B	14	E	34	E	54	B
15	B	35	C	55	A	15	B	35	E	55	A
16	B	36	E	56	C	16	B	36	B	56	A
17	A	37	E	57		17	D	37	E	57	
18	E	38	A	58		18	C	38	D	58	
19	B	39	D	59		19	C	39	C	59	
20	A	40	A	60		20	E	40	A	60	

Praxis Core Math Practice Test 1

1) Choice C is correct

Add the first 5 numbers. $40 + 45 + 50 + 35 + 55 = 225$, To find the distance traveled in the next 5 hours, multiply the average by number of hours. $Distance = Average \times Rate = 65 \times 5 = 325$. Add both numbers. $325 + 225 = 550$

2) Choice B is correct

Use distance formula: $Distance = Rate \times time \Rightarrow 420 = 65 \times T$, divide both sides by 65. $420 \div 65 = T \Rightarrow T = 6.4\ hours$. Change hours to minutes for the decimal part. $0.4\ hours = 0.4 \times 60 = 24\ minutes$.

3) Choice D is correct

Use Pythagorean Theorem: $a^2 + b^2 = c^2 \Rightarrow 5^2 + 12^2 = c^2 \Rightarrow 169 = c^2 \Rightarrow c = 13$

4) Choice D is correct

Of the 30 employees, there are 5 females under age 45 and 6 males age 45 or older. Therefore, the probability that the person selected will be either a female under age 45 or a male age 45 or older is: $\frac{5}{30} + \frac{6}{30} = \frac{11}{30}$

5) Choice E is correct

Use FOIL (First, Out, In, Last). $(7x + 2y)(5x + 2y) = 35x^2 + 14xy + 10xy + 4y^2 =$

$$35x^2 + 24xy + 4y^2$$

6) Choice E is correct

Use distributive property: $5x(4 + 2y) = 20x + 10xy$

7) Choice E is correct

$y = 5ab + 3b^3$. Plug in the values of a and b in the equation: $a = 2$ and $b = 3$.

$y = 5\ (2)(3) + 3\ (3)^3 = 30 + 3(27) = 30 + 81 = 111$

8) Choice D is correct

x and z are colinear. y and $5x$ are colinear. Therefore,

$x + z = y + 5x, subtract\ x\ from\ both\ sides, then, z = y + 4x$

9) Choice E is correct

The perimeter of the trapezoid is 64. Therefore, the missing side (height) is

$= 64 - 18 - 12 - 14 = 20$. Area of the trapezoid: $A = \frac{1}{2}\, h\, (b_1 + b_2) =$

$$\frac{1}{2}\,(20)\,(12 + 14) = 260$$

10) Choice C is correct

Let x be the number. Write the equation and solve for x. $\frac{2}{3} \times 15 = \frac{2}{5} \cdot x \Rightarrow \frac{2 \times 15}{3} = \frac{2x}{5}$, use cross multiplication to solve for x. $5 \times 30 = 2x \times 3 \Rightarrow 150 = 6x \Rightarrow x = 25$

11) Choice B is correct

To find the discount, multiply the number by $(100\% - rate\ of\ discount)$. Therefore, for the first discount we get: $(D)\,(100\% - 25\%) = (D)(0.75) = 0.75$. For increase of 10%: $(0.75\,D)(100\% + 10\%) = (0.75\,D)(1.10) = 0.82\,D = 82\%\ of\ D$ or $0.82\,D$.

12) The answer is 10

$\frac{y}{5} = x - \frac{2}{5}x + 2$, Multiply both sides of the equation by 5. Then:$5 \times \frac{y}{5} = 5 \times \left(x - \frac{2}{5}x + 2\right) \rightarrow$ $y = 5x - 2x + 10 \rightarrow y = 3x + 10$, now, subtract $3x$ from both sides of the equation. Then:

$y - 3x = 10$

13) The answer is 1.75

First, factorize the numerator and simplify.$\frac{x^2-16}{x+4} + 3(x + 4) = 15 \rightarrow \frac{(x-4)(x+4)}{x+4} + 3x + 12 = 15$

Divide both sides of the fraction by $(x + 4)$. Then:$x - 4 + 3x + 12 = 15 \rightarrow 4x + 8 = 15$

Subtract 8 from both sides of the equation. Then: $\rightarrow 4x = 15 - 8 = 7 \rightarrow x = \frac{7}{4}$ or $x = 1.75$

14) The answer is 45

Let L be the length of the rectangular and W be the with of the rectangular. Then,

$L = 4W + 3$, The perimeter of the rectangle is 36 meters. Therefore:

$2L + 2W = 36$, $L + W = 18$, Replace the value of L from the first equation into the second equation and solve for W:$(4W + 3) + W = 18 \rightarrow 5W + 3 = 18 \rightarrow 5W = 15 \rightarrow W = 3$

The width of the rectangle is 3 meters and its length is:$L = 4W + 3 = 4(3) + 3 = 15$

The area of the rectangle is: $length \times width = 3 \times 15 = 45$

15) Choice B is correct

Use the formula of areas of circles. $Area = \pi r^2 \Rightarrow 49\pi = \pi r^2 \Rightarrow 49 = r^2 \Rightarrow r = 7$

Praxis Core Math Prep 2020-2021

Radius of the circle is 7. Now, use the circumference formula: Circumference =

$$2\pi r = 2\pi\,(7) = 14\,\pi$$

16) Choice B is correct

Use the formula for Percent of Change. $\dfrac{\text{New Value} - \text{Old Value}}{\text{Old Value}} \times 100\%$.

$\dfrac{28-50}{50} \times 100\,\% = -44\%$ (negative sign here means that the new price is less than old price).

17) Choice A is correct

Let x be the number of years. Therefore, \$2,000 per year equals $2000x$. starting from \$26,000 annual salary means you should add that amount to $2000x$. Income more than that is:

$I > 2000\,x\,+\,26000$

18) Choice E is correct

Use the information provided in the question to draw the shape.

Use Pythagorean Theorem: $a^2 + b^2 = c^2$

$60^2 + 80^2 = c^2 \Rightarrow 3600 + 6400 = c^2 \Rightarrow 10000 = c^2 \Rightarrow c = 100$

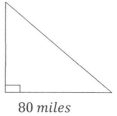

60 *miles*

80 *miles*

19) Choice B is correct

The question is this: 530.40 is what percent of 631?

$percent = \dfrac{530.40}{631} = 84.05 \cong 84.$ 530.40 is 84% of 631. Therefore, the discount is:

$100\% - 84\% = 16\%$

20) Choice A is correct

If the score of Mia was 40, therefore the score of Ava is 20. Since, the score of Emma was half as that of Ava, therefore, the score of Emma is 10.

21) Choice D is correct

If 17 balls are removed from the bag at random, there will be one ball in the bag. The probability of choosing a brown ball is 1 out of 18. Therefore, the probability of not choosing a brown ball is 17 out of 18 and the probability of having not a brown ball after removing 17 balls is the same.

22) Choice C is correct

Let x be the smallest number. Then, these are the numbers: $x, x + 1, x + 2, x + 3, x + 4$

$average = \dfrac{\text{sum of terms}}{\text{number of terms}} \Rightarrow 36 = \dfrac{x+(x+1)+(x+2)+(x+3)+(x+4)}{5} \Rightarrow 36 = \dfrac{5x+10}{5} \Rightarrow$

$$180 = 5x + 10 \Rightarrow 170 = 5x \Rightarrow x = 34$$

23) Choice C is correct

Use this formula: Percent of Change: $\dfrac{\text{New Value} - \text{Old Value}}{\text{Old Value}} \times 100\%$.

$\dfrac{18,200 - 28,000}{28,000} \times 100\% = -35\%$. The negative sign means that the price decreased

24) Choice D is correct

If the length of the box is 36, then the width of the box is one third of it, 12, and the height of the box is 4 (one third of the width). The volume of the box is: $V = lwh = (36)(12)(4) = 1,728$

25) Choice A is correct

Write a proportion and solve for the missing number. $\dfrac{32}{12} = \dfrac{6}{x} \rightarrow 32x = 6 \times 12 = 72$

$32x = 72 \rightarrow x = \dfrac{72}{32} = 2.25$

26) Choice C is correct

Let x be the number. Write the equation and solve for x. $(28 - x) \div x = 3$

Multiply both sides by x. $(28 - x) = 3x$, then add x both sides. $28 = 4x$, now divide both sides by 4. $x = 7$

27) Choice B is correct

The sum of supplement angles is 180. Let x be that angle. Therefore, $x + 9x = 180$

$10x = 180$, divide both sides by 10: $x = 18$

28) Choice C is correct

The average speed of john is: $150 \div 6 = 25$, The average speed of Alice is: $140 \div 4 = 35$

Write the ratio and simplify. $25:35 \Rightarrow 5:7$

29) The answer is: -64

Use PEMDAS (order of operation): $[3 \times (-14) - 48] - 14 + [3 \times 8] \div 2 =$

$$[-42 - 48] + 14 + 24 \div 2 = -90 + 14 + 12 = -64$$

30) The answer is 2.5

First, use distribute property to simplify $-4(x + 2)$. $\qquad -4(x + 2) = -4x - 8$

Now, combine like terms: $x - 4(x + 2) = -15.5 \rightarrow x - 4x - 8 = -15.5 \rightarrow -3x - 8 = -15.5$

Add 8 to both sides of the equation: $-3x - 8 + 8 = -15.5 + 8 \rightarrow -3x = -7.5$. Divide both sides by -3. Then: $-3x = -7.5 \rightarrow \dfrac{-3x}{-3} = \dfrac{-7.5}{-3} \rightarrow x = 2.5$

31) Choice B is correct

$$average\ (mean) = \frac{sum\ of\ terms}{number\ of\ terms} = \frac{8+11+14+16+1\ .5+16+14.5}{7} = 14.14$$

32) Choice B is correct

6% of the volume of the solution is alcohol. Let x be the volume of the solution.

Then: $6\%\ of\ x = 24\ ml \Rightarrow 0.06\ x = 24 \Rightarrow x = 24 \div 0.06 = 400$

33) Choice B is correct

$average = \frac{sum\ of\ terms}{number\ of\ terms}$. The sum of the weight of all girls is: $18 \times 56 = 1,008\ kg$

The sum of the weight of all boys is: $32 \times 62 = 1,984\ kg$. The sum of the weight of all students is: $1,008 + 1,984 = 2,992\ kg$. $average = \frac{2992}{50} = 59.84$

34) Choice D is correct

Let x be the original price. If the price of a laptop is decreased by 20% to \$360, then: $80\%\ of$

$x = 360 \Rightarrow 0.80x = 360 \Rightarrow x = 360 \div 0.80 = 450$

35) Choice C is correct

Use simple interest formula: $I = prt$. (I = interest, p = principal, r = rate, t = time). $I = (9,000)(0.045)(5) = 2,025$

36) Choice E is correct

$(2.9 \times 10^6) \times (2.6 \times 10^{-5}) = (2.9 \times 2.6) \times (10^6 \times 10^{-5}) = 7.54 \times (10^{6+(-5)})$
$$= 7.54 \times 10^1$$

37) Choice E is correct

The formula of the volume of pyramid is: $V = \frac{l \times w \times h}{3}$

The length and width of the pyramid is $6\ cm$ and its height is $14\ cm$. Therefore:

$$V = \frac{6 \times 6 \times 14}{3} = 168\ cm^3$$

38) Choice A is correct

Let x be the integer. Then: $2x - 5 = 73$, Add 5 both sides: $2x = 78$, Divide both sides by 2: $x = 39$

39) Choice D is correct

To find the discount, multiply the number by $(100\% - ate\ of\ discount)$. Therefore, for the first discount we get: $(300)(100\% - 15\%) = (300)(0.85)$. For the next 15% discount: $(300)(0.85)(0.85)$.

40) Choice A is correct

Plug in each pair of number in the equation: $2x + 4y = 8$

A. $(2, 1)$: $2(2) + 4(1) = 8$
B. $(-1, 3)$: $2(-1) + 4(3) = 10$
C. $(-2, 2)$: $2(-2) + 4(2) = 4$
D. $(2, 2)$: $2(2) + 4(2) = 12$
E. $(2, 8)$: $2(2) + 4(8) = 36$

Only choice A is correct.

41) Choice C is correct

Plugin the values of x and y provided in the choices into both equations. Let's start with $2x + 2y = 2$:

A. $(1, 3)$ $2x + 2y = 2 \rightarrow 2 + 6 \neq 2$
B. $(2, 4)$ $2x + y = 2 \rightarrow 4 + 8 \neq 2$
C. $(2, -1)$ $2x + 2y = 2 \rightarrow 4 + (-2) = 2$
D. $(4, -6)$ $2x + 2y = 2 \rightarrow 12 + (-12) \neq 2$
E. $(1, -6)$ $2x + 2y = 2 \rightarrow 2 + (-12) \neq 2$

Only choice C is correct.

42) Choice A is correct

If $f(x) = 3x + 4(x + 1) + 2$, then find $f(4x)$ by substituting $4x$ for every x in the function. This gives: $f(4x) = 3(4x) + 4(4x + 1) + 2$

It simplifies to: $f(4x) = 3(4x) + 4(4x + 1) + 2 = 12x + 16x + 4 + 2 = 28x + 6$

43) Choice C is correct

First, find the equation of the line. All lines through the origin are of the form $y = mx$, so the equation is $y = \frac{1}{3}x$. Of the given choices, only choice C (9,3), satisfies this equation:

$y = \frac{1}{3}x \rightarrow 3 = \frac{1}{3}(9) = 3$

44) Choice C is correct

$(3n^2 + 2n + 6) - (2n^2 - 4)$. Add like terms together: $3n^2 - 2n^2 = n^2$, $2n$ doesn't have like terms. $6 - (-4) = 10$, Combine these terms into one expression to find the answer:

$n^2 + 2n + 10$

45) Choice C is correct

Simplify and solve for x in the equation. $4(x + 1) = 6(x - 4) + 20$, $4x + 4 = 6x - 24 + 20$, $4x + 4 = 6x - 4$. Subtract $4x$ from both sides: $4 = 2x - 4$, Add 4 to both sides: $8 = 2x$, $4 = x$

46) Choice A is correct

To rewrite $\dfrac{1}{\frac{1}{x-5}+\frac{1}{x+4}}$, first simplify $\dfrac{1}{x-5} + \dfrac{1}{x+4}$.

172

$$\frac{1}{x-5} + \frac{1}{x+4} = \frac{1(x+4)}{(x-5)(x+4)} + \frac{1(x-5)}{(x+4)(x-5)} = \frac{(x+4)+(x-5)}{(x+4)(x-5)}$$

Then: $\frac{1}{\frac{1}{x-5}+\frac{1}{x+4}} = \frac{1}{\frac{(x+4)+(x-5)}{(x+4)(x-5)}} = \frac{(x-5)(x+4)}{(x-5)+(x+4)}$. (Remember, $\frac{1}{\frac{1}{x}} = x$)

This result is equivalent to the expression in choice A.

47) Choice B is correct

Since $(0, 0)$ is a solution to the system of inequalities, substituting 0 for x and 0 for y in the given system must result in two true inequalities. After this substitution, $y < c - x$ becomes $0 < a$, and $y > x + b$ becomes $0 > b$. Hence, a is positive and b is negative.
Therefore, $c > b$.

48) Choice D is correct

$3x + 10 = 46 \rightarrow 3x = 46 - 10 = 36 \rightarrow x = \frac{36}{3} = 12$

49) Choice B is correct

The input value is 5. Then: $x = 5$. $f(x) = x^2 - 3x \rightarrow f(5) = 5^2 - 3(5) = 25 - 15 = 10$

50) Choice C is correct

Multiplying each side of $\frac{4}{x} = \frac{12}{x-8}$ by $x(x - 8)$ gives $4(x - 8) = 12(x)$, distributing the 4 over the values within the parentheses yields $x - 8 = 3x$ or $x = -4$.

Therefore, the value of $\frac{x}{2} = \frac{-4}{2} = -2$.

51) The answer is 97.6
The area of the square is 595.36. Therefore, the side of the square is square root of the area.

$\sqrt{595.36} = 24.4$.   Four times the side of the square is the perimeter: $4 \times 24.4 = 97.6$

52) The answer is 8
Use formula of rectangle prism volume. $V = (length)(width)(height) \Rightarrow$

$2000 = (25)(10)(height) \Rightarrow height = 2,000 \div 250 = 8$

53) Choice C is correct

Let x be all expenses, then $\frac{22}{100}x = \$660 \rightarrow x = \frac{100 \times \$660}{22} = \$3,000$

Mr. Jones spent for his rent: $\frac{27}{100} \times \$3,000 = \$810$

54) Choice B is correct

It is given that $g(5) = 4$. Therefore, to find the value of $f(g(5))$, then $f(g(5)) = f(4) = 6$

55) Choice A is correct

Area of the triangle is: $\frac{1}{2} AD \times BC$ and AD is perpendicular to BC. Triangle ADC is a

$30° - 60° - 90°$ right triangle. The relationship among all sides of right triangle $30° - 60° - 90°$ is provided in the following triangle: In this triangle, the opposite side of $30°$ angle is half of the hypotenuse. And the opposite side of $60°$ is opposite of $30° × \sqrt{3}$

$CD = 6$, then $AD = 6 × \sqrt{3}$

Area of the triangle ABC is: $\frac{1}{2} AD × BC = \frac{1}{2} 6\sqrt{3} × 12 = 36\sqrt{3}$

56) Choice C is correct

$6 \blacksquare 28 = \sqrt{6^2 + 28} = \sqrt{36 + 28} = \sqrt{64} = 8$

Praxis Core Math Practice Test 2

1) Choice C is correct

$average \ (mean) = \frac{\text{sum of terms}}{\text{number of terms}} \Rightarrow 90 = \frac{sum \ of \ terms}{50} \Rightarrow sum = 90 × 50 = 4500$

The difference of 94 and 69 is 25. Therefore, 25 should be subtracted from the sum.

$4500 - 25 = 4475, \ mean = \frac{\text{sum of terms}}{\text{number of terms}} \Rightarrow mean = \frac{4475}{50} = 89.5$

2) Choice D is correct

For sum of 5: $(1 \ \& \ 4) \ and \ (4 \ \& \ 1), (2 \ \& \ 3)$ and $(3 \ \& \ 2)$, therefore we have 4 options.
For sum of 8: $(5 \ \& \ 3) and \ (3 \ \& \ 5), (4 \ \& \ 4)$ and $(2 \ \& \ 6)$, and $(6 \ \& \ 2)$, we have 5 options. To get a sum of 5 or 8 for two dice: $4 + 5 = 9$. Since, we have $6 × 6 = 36$ total number of options, the probability of getting a sum of 5 and 8 is 9 out of 36 or $\frac{9}{36} = \frac{1}{4}$

3) Choice D is correct

Use FOIL method. $(5x + 2y)(2x - y) = 10x^2 - 5xy + 4xy - 2y^2 = 10x^2 - xy - 2y^2$

4) Choice D is correct

To solve absolute values equations, write two equations. $x - 10$ could be positive 4, or negative 4. Therefore, $x - 10 = 4 \Rightarrow x = 14, \ x - 10 = -4 \Rightarrow x = 6$. Find the product of solutions: $6 × 14 = 84$

5) Choice B is correct

The equation of a line in slope intercept form is: $y = mx + b$. Solve for y.

$4x - 2y = 6 \Rightarrow -2y = 6 - 4x \Rightarrow y = (6 - 4x) ÷ (-2) \Rightarrow y = 2x - 3$. The slope is 2.

The slope of the line perpendicular to this line is: $m_1 × m_2 = -1 \Rightarrow 2 × m_2 = -1 \Rightarrow m_2 = -\frac{1}{2}$.

6) Choice C is correct

Plug in the value of x and y. $x = 3$ and $y = -2$.

$6(x - 2y) + (2 - x)^2 = 6(3 - 2(-2)) + (2 - 3)^2 = 6(3 + 4) + (-1)^2 = 42 + 1 = 43$

7) Choice E is correct

Use formula of rectangle prism volume. $V = (length)\,(width)\,(height) \Rightarrow 2500 = (25)\,(10)\,(height) \Rightarrow height = 2500 \div 250 = 10$

8) Choice C is correct

$4 \div \dfrac{1}{3} = 12$

9) Choice B is correct

The diagonal of the square is 4. Let x be the side. Use Pythagorean Theorem: $a^2 + b^2 = c^2$

$x^2 + x^2 = 4^2 \Rightarrow 2x^2 = 4^2 \Rightarrow 2x^2 = 16 \Rightarrow x^2 = 8 \Rightarrow x = \sqrt{8}$

The area of the square is: $\sqrt{8} \times \sqrt{8} = 8$

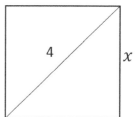

10) Choice D is correct

Solve for the sum of five numbers.

$$average = \frac{sum\ of\ terms}{number\ of\ terms} \Rightarrow 26 = \frac{sum\ of\ 5\ numbers}{5} \Rightarrow sum\ of\ 5\ numbers = 26 \times 5 = 130$$

The sum of 5 numbers is 130. If a sixth number 42 is added, then the sum of 6 numbers is

$130 + 42 = 172.\ average = \frac{sum\ of\ terms}{number\ of\ terms} = \frac{172}{6} = 28.66$

11) Choice B is correct

ratio of A: $\frac{570}{600} = 0.95$ ratio of B: $\frac{291}{300} = 0.97$ ratio of C: $\frac{665}{700} = 0.95$ ratio of D: $\frac{528}{550} = 0.96$

The maximum ratio is 0.97

12) Choice E is correct

First find percentage of men in city A and percentage of women in city C. Percentage of men in

city A $= \frac{600}{1170}$ and percentage of women in city C $= \frac{665}{1365}$. Find the ratio and simplify. $\frac{\frac{600}{1170}}{\frac{665}{1365}} = \frac{20}{19}$

13) Choice C is correct

$\dfrac{528 + x}{550} = 1.2 \rightarrow 528 + x = 660 \rightarrow x = 132$

14) Choice E is correct

Jason needs an 70% average to pass for five exams. Therefore, the sum of 5 exams must be at lease $5 \times 70 = 350$.The sum of 4 exams is: $68 + 72 + 85 + 90 = 315$.

The minimum score Jason can earn on his fifth and final test to pass is: $350 - 315 = 35$

15) Choice B is correct

Isolate and solve for $x.\frac{2}{3}x + \frac{1}{6} = \frac{1}{2} \Rightarrow \frac{2}{3}x = \frac{1}{2} - \frac{1}{6} = \frac{1}{3} \Rightarrow \frac{2}{3}x = \frac{1}{3}$ .Multiply both sides by the reciprocal of the coefficient of x. $(\frac{3}{2})\frac{2}{3}x = \frac{1}{3}(\frac{3}{2}) \Rightarrow x = \frac{3}{6} = \frac{1}{2}$

16) Choice B is correct

Use simple interest formula:$I = prt$ (I = interest, p = principal, r = rate, t = time).

$$I = (12,000)(0.045)(2) = 1,080$$

17) Choice D is correct

Simplify. $7x^2y^3(2x^2y)^3= 7x^2y^3(8x^6y^3) = 56x^8y^6$

18) Choice C is correct

y is the intersection of the three circles. Therefore, it must be even (from circle A), negative (from circle B), and multiple of 6 (from circle C). From the choice, only -6 is even, negative and multiple of 6.

19) Choice C is correct

Three times of 25,000 is 75,000. One sixth of them cancelled their tickets. One sixth of 75,000 equals 12,500 ($\frac{1}{6} \times 75000 = 12500$). 62,500 ($75000 - 12000 = 62500$) fans are attending this week.

20) Choice E is correct

The area of the square is 49 inches. Therefore, the side of the square is square root of the area.

$\sqrt{49} = 7$ inches. Four times the side of the square is the perimeter: $4 \times 7 = 28\ inches$

21) Choice E is correct

$g(x) = -4,$ **then** $f(g(x)) = f(-4) = 2(-4)^3 + 5(-4)^2 + 2(-4) = -128 + 80 - 8 = -56$

22) Choice E is correct

Use the information provided in the question to draw the shape.

Use Pythagorean Theorem: $a^2 + b^2 = c^2$

$50^2 + 120^2 = c^2 \Rightarrow 2,500 + 14,400 = c^2 \Rightarrow 16,900 = c^2 \Rightarrow c = 130$

120 $mile$

Port A

50 $miles$

176

23) Choice B is correct

Plug in 104 for F and then solve for C.

$$C = \frac{5}{9}(F - 32) \Rightarrow C = \frac{5}{9}(104 - 32) \Rightarrow C = \frac{5}{9}(72) = 40$$

24) Choice A is correct

The width of the rectangle is twice its length. Let x be the length. Then, $width = 2x$

Perimeter of the rectangle is $2\,(width + length) = 2(2x + x) = 72 \Rightarrow 6x = 72 \Rightarrow x = 12$. Length of the rectangle is 12 meters.

25) Choice D is correct

$average = \frac{\text{sum of terms}}{\text{number of terms}} \Rightarrow$ (average of 6 numbers) $14 = \frac{\text{sum of numbers}}{6} \Rightarrow$ sum of 6 numbers is $14 \times 6 = 84$, (average of 4 numbers) $10 = \frac{\text{sum of numbers}}{4} \Rightarrow$ sum of 4 numbers is $10 \times 4 = 40$. $sum\ of\ 6\ numbers - sum\ of\ 4\ numbers = sum\ of\ 2\ numbers$,

$84 - 40 = 44$ average of 2 numbers $= \frac{44}{2} = 22$

26) Choice A is correct

First, find the number. Let x be the number. Write the equation and solve for x. 150% of a number is 75, then: $1.5 \times x = 75 \Rightarrow x = 75 \div 1.5 = 50$, 80% of 50 is: $0.8 \times 50 = 40$

27) Choice E is correct

Solve for y. $4x - 2y = 12 \Rightarrow -2y = 12 - 4x \Rightarrow y = 2x - 6$. The slope of the line is 2.

28) Choice B is correct

the population is increased by 10% and 20%. 10% increase changes the population to 110% of original population. For the second increase, multiply the result by 120%.

$(1.10) \times (1.20) = 1.32 = 132\%$. 32 percent of the population is increased after two years.

29) Choice C is correct

The formula for the area of the circle is: $A = \pi r^2$ **,The area is 36π. Therefore:** $A = \pi r^2 \Rightarrow 6\pi = \pi r^2$, **Divide both sides by** π: $36 = r^2 \Rightarrow r = 6$. Diameter of a circle is $2 \times$ radius. Then:

$Diameter = 2 \times 6 = 12$

30) Choice D is correct

If 20% of a number is 4, what is the number: $20\%\ of\ x = 4 \Rightarrow 0.20\,x = 4 \Rightarrow x = 4 \div 0.20 = 20$

31) Choice C is correct

Write a proportion and solve for x. $\frac{3}{2} = \frac{x}{26} \Rightarrow 2x = 3 \times 26 \Rightarrow x = 39\ ft$

32) Choice C is correct

The distance between Jason and Joe is 9 $miles$. Jason running at 6.5 $miles\ per\ hour$ and Joe is running at the speed of 8 $miles\ per\ hour$. Therefore, every hour the distance is 1.5 $miles$ less.

$9 \div 1.5 = 6$

33) Choice D is correct

The failing rate is 11 out of 44 $= \frac{11}{44}$, Change the fraction to percent: $\frac{11}{44} \times 100\% = 25\%$. 25 percent of students failed. Therefore, 75 percent of students passed the exam.

34) Choice E is correct

$g(x) = -3$, then $f\big(g(x)\big) = f(-3) = 2\,(-3)^3 + 5(-3)^2 + 2(-3) = -54 + 45 - 6 = -15$

35) Choice E is correct

Let x be the width of the rectangle. Use Pythagorean Theorem:

$a^2 + b^2 = c^2$

$x^2 + 6^2 = 10^2 \Rightarrow x^2 + 36 = 100 \Rightarrow x^2 = 100 - 36 = 64 \Rightarrow x = 8$

Perimeter of the rectangle $= 2\,(length\ +\ width) = 2\,(8 + 6) = 2\,(14) = 28$

36) Choice B is correct

The perimeter of the trapezoid is 40. herefore, the missing side (height) is

$= 40 - 8 - 12 - 6 = 14$. Area of a trapezoid: $A = \frac{1}{2}\,h\,(b_1 + b_2) = \frac{1}{2}\,(14)\,(6 + 8) = 98$

37) Choice E is correct

$f\big(g(x)\big) = 2 \times (\frac{1}{x})^3 + 2 = \frac{2}{x^3} + 2$

38) Choice D is correct

Use the information provided in the question to draw the shape.

Use Pythagorean Theorem: $a^2 + b^2 = c^2$

$80^2 + 150^2 = c^2 \Rightarrow 6400 + 22500 = c^2 \Rightarrow 28900 = c^2 \Rightarrow c = 170$

39) Choice C is correct

Write the ratio of $5a$ to $2b$. $\frac{5a}{2b} = \frac{1}{10}$. Use cross multiplication and then simplify.

150 miles

Port A

80 miles

$$5a \times 10 = 2b \times 1 \rightarrow 50a = 2b \rightarrow a = \frac{2b}{50} = \frac{b}{25}$$

Now, find the ratio of a to b. $\frac{a}{b} = \frac{\frac{b}{25}}{b} \rightarrow \frac{b}{25} \div b = \frac{b}{25} \times \frac{1}{b} = \frac{b}{25b} = \frac{1}{25}$

40) Choice A is correct

Plug in the value of x in the equation and solve for y. $2y = \frac{2x^2}{3} + 6 \rightarrow 2y = \frac{2(9)^2}{3} + 6 \rightarrow$

$$2y = \frac{2(81)}{3} + 6 \rightarrow 2y = 54 + 6 = 60 \rightarrow 2y = 60 \rightarrow y = 30$$

41) Choice D is correct

Since $N = 6$, substitute 6 for N in the equation $\frac{x-3}{5} = N$, which gives $\frac{x-3}{5} = 6$. Multiplying both sides of $\frac{x-3}{5} = 6$ by 5 gives $x - 3 = 30$ and then adding 3 to both sides of $x - 3 = 30$ then, $x = 33$.

42) Choice C is correct

$b^{\frac{m}{n}} = \sqrt[n]{b^m}$ For any positive integers m and n. Thus, $b^{\frac{3}{5}} = \sqrt[5]{b^3}$

43) Choice B is correct

The total number of pages read by Sara is 3 (hours she spent reading) multiplied by her rate of reading: $\frac{N pages}{hour} \times 3 hours = 3N$

Similarly, the total number of pages read by Mary is 4 (hours she spent reading) multiplied by her rate of reading: $\frac{M pages}{hour} \times 4 hours = 4M$ the total number of pages read by Sara and Mary is the sum of the total number of pages read by Sara and the total number of pages read by Mary: $3N + 4M$.

44) Choices D and E are correct
First, find the sum of five numbers.

$\text{average} = \frac{\text{sum of terms}}{\text{number of terms}} \Rightarrow 25 = \frac{\text{sum of 5 numbers}}{5} \Rightarrow \text{sum of 5 numbers} = 25 \times 5 = 125$

The sum of 5 numbers is 125. If a sixth number that is greater than 42 is added to these numbers, then the sum of 6 numbers must be greater than 162. $125 + 42 = 167$

If the number was 42, then the average of the numbers is:

$\text{average} = \frac{\text{sum of terms}}{\text{number of terms}} = \frac{167}{6} = 27.83$

Since the number is bigger than 42. Then, the average of six numbers must be greater than 27.83.

Choices D and E are greater than 27.83.

45) The answer is 28.
Let x be the width of the rectangle. Use Pythagorean Theorem:

$$a^2 + b^2 = c^2$$

$$x^2 + 8^2 = 10^2 \Rightarrow x^2 + 64 = 100 \Rightarrow x^2 = 100 - 64 = 36 \Rightarrow x = 6$$

Perimeter of the rectangle $= 2\ (length\ +\ width)\ = 2\ (8\ +\ 6) = 2\ (14) = 28$

46) Choice D is correct
Solving Systems of Equations by Elimination: Multiply the first equation by (-2), then add it to the second equation.

$$\begin{array}{l} -2(2x + 5y = 11) \\ \underline{4x - 2y = -14} \end{array} \Rightarrow \begin{array}{l} -4x - 10y = -22 \\ 4x - 2y = -14 \end{array} \Rightarrow -12y = -36 \Rightarrow y = 3$$

Plug in the value of y into one of the equations and solve for x.

$$2x + 5(3) = 11 \Rightarrow 2x + 15 = 11 \Rightarrow 2x = -4 \Rightarrow x = -2$$

47) Choice A is correct

Identify the input value. Since the function is in the form $f(x)$ and the question asks to calculate $f(4)$, the input value is four. $f(4) \rightarrow x = 4$, Using the function, input the desired x value. Now substitute 4 in for every x in the function. $f(x) = 3x^2 - 4$, $f(4) = 3(4)^2 - 4$, $f(4) = 48 - 4$, $f(4) = 44$

48) Choice D is correct
Frist factor the function: $f(x) = x^3 + 5x^2 + 6x = x\ (x + 2)(x + 3)$**, To find the zeros,** $f(x)$ **should be zero.** $f(x) = x\ (x + 2)(x + 3) = 0$**, Therefore, the zeros are:** $x = 0,\ (x + 2) = 0 \Rightarrow x = -2, (x + 3) = 0 \Rightarrow x = -3$

49) **The answer is:** -30
Use PEMDAS (order of operation):

$$5 + 8 \times (-2) - [4\ +\ 22\ \times 5] \div 6 = 5 + 8 \times (-2) - [4\ +\ 110] \div\ 6$$
$$= 5 + 8\ \times (-2) - [114] \div 6 = 5 + (-16) - 19 = 5 + (-16) - 19$$
$$= -11 - 19 = -30$$

50) Choice D and E are correct
The equation of a line is in the form of $y = mx + b$, where m is the slope of the line and b is the $y - intercept$ of the line. Two points $(1, 2)$ and $(-1, 6)$ are on line A. Therefore, the slope of the line A is: $slope\ of\ line\ A = \frac{y_2 - y_1}{x_2 - x_1} = \frac{6-2}{-1-1} = \frac{4}{-2} = -2$

The slope of line A is -2. Thus, the formula of the line A is: $y = mx + b = -2x + b$, choose a point and plug in the values of x and y in the equation to solve for b. Let's choose point $(1, 2)$. Then: $y = -2x + b \rightarrow 2 = -2(1) + b \rightarrow b = 2 + 2 = 4$. The equation of line A is: $y = -2x + 4$

Now, let's review the choices provided:

A. $(-1, 2)$ $y = -2x + 4 \rightarrow 2 = -2(-1) + 4 = 6$ This is not true.

B. $(5, 7)$ $y = -2x + 4 \rightarrow 7 = -2(5) + 4 = -6$ This is not true.

C. $(3, 4)$ $y = -2x + 4 \rightarrow 4 = -2(3) + 4 = -2$ This is not true.

180

D. $(3, -2)$ $y = -2x + 4 \rightarrow -2 = -2(3) + 4 = -2$ This is true!

E. $(6, -8)$ $y = -2x + 4 \rightarrow -8 = -2(6) + 4 = -8$ This is true!

51) Choice C is correct

If $x - a$ is a factor of $g(x)$, then $g(a)$ must equal 0. Based on the table $g(2) = 0$. Therefore, $x - 2$ must be a factor of $g(x)$.

52) Choice C is correct

To solve this problem first solve the equation for c. $\frac{c}{b} = 2$

Multiply by b on both sides. Then: $b \times \frac{c}{b} = 2 \times b \rightarrow c = 2b$.   Now to calculate $\frac{4b}{c}$,

substitute the value for c into the denominator and simplify. $\frac{4b}{c} = \frac{4b}{2b} = \frac{4}{2} = \frac{2}{1} = 2$

53) Choice B is correct

$x + 5 = 8 \rightarrow x = 8 - 5 = 3, 2y - 1 = 5 \rightarrow 2y = 6 \rightarrow y = 3, xy + 15 = 3 \times 3 + 15 = 24$

54) Choice B is correct

The equation $\frac{a-b}{b} = \frac{10}{13}$ can be rewritten as $\frac{a}{b} - \frac{b}{b} = \frac{10}{13}$, from which it follows that $\frac{a}{b} - 1 = \frac{10}{13}$, or $\frac{a}{b} = \frac{10}{13} + 1 = \frac{23}{13}$.

55) Choice A is correct

First write the equation in slope intercept form. Add $2x$ to both sides to get $6y = 2x + 24$. Now divide both sides by 6 to get $y = \frac{1}{3}x + 4$. The slope of this line is $\frac{1}{3}$, so any line that also has a slope of $\frac{1}{3}$ would be parallel to it. Only choice A has a slope of $\frac{1}{3}$.

56) Choice A is correct

Since a box of pen costs \$3, then $3p$ Represents the cost of p boxes of pen. Multiplying this number times 1.085 will increase the cost by the 8.5% for tax. Then add the \$6 shipping fee for the total: $1.085(3p) + 6$

www.EffortlessMath.com

... So Much More Online!

✓ FREE Math lessons

✓ More Math learning books!

✓ Mathematics Worksheets

✓ Online Math Tutors

Need a PDF version of this book?

Visit www.EffortlessMath.com

Praxis Core Math Prep 2020-2021

Receive the PDF version of this book or get another FREE book!

Thank you for using our Book!

Do you LOVE this book?

Then, you can get the PDF version of this book or another book absolutely FREE!

Please email us at:

info@EffortlessMath.com

for details.

Made in the USA
Monee, IL
05 November 2020

46811138R00103